WIND
and
WAVES

WIND
and
WAVES

A NOVEL BY
YASUSHI INOUE

Translated by
James T. Araki

University of Hawaii Press • Honolulu

Fūtō by Yasushi Inoue
© 1963 Yasushi Inoue
Originally published in Japan

English translation
© 1989 University of Hawaii Press

Library of Congress Cataloging-in-Publication Data

Inoue, Yasushi, 1907–
   [Fūtō. English]
   Wind and waves : a novel / Yasushi Inoue : translated by James T.
Araki.
        p.   cm.
   Translation of: Fūtō.
   ISBN 0-8248-1178-X
   1. Korea—History—Koryŏ period, 935–1392—Fiction. 2. Korea–
–History—Mongolian invasions, 1231–1270—Fiction. 3. Japan–
–History—Attempted Mongol invasions, 1274–1281—Fiction.
I. Title.
PL830.N63F8413 1989   88–27842
895.6'35—dc19   CIP

∞ *The paper used in this publication meets the minimum requirements of
American National Standard for Information Sciences—Permanence of Paper for
Printed Library Materials*

ANSI Z39.48-1984

CONTENTS

PREFACE

Wind and Waves tells the dramatic story of the great events that affected all of East Asia during the middle decades of the thirteenth century as Kubilai Khan, ruler of the Mongol hordes, overthrew the Sung Dynasty of China, then turned his thoughts eastward, coveting Japan, a small bellicose nation of warrior samurai united under the shogun in Kamakura. The setting of the novel is the kingdom of Koryŏ (the land known today as Korea). Devastated repeatedly by Mongol armies intent on pounding the stubborn peninsular nation into submission, Koryŏ finds itself seduced and then seized upon by Kubilai as the staging area for an invasion of Japan. Never before has the story of this extraordinary period in the history of Korea been narrated so fully, or with such poignancy and so much understanding of the suffering of the Koreans at a time when they were threatened with extinction as a culturally identifiable people.

Wind and Waves was published in Japan in 1963, and won the Yomiuri Literary Prize for the following year. It is among the finest works of Yasushi Inoue, today esteemed as the most distinguished among Japan's contemporary novelists. Inoue's knowledge of the broad sweep of Mongol impact in Central and East Asia is authoritative; it has enabled him to see the era of Kubilai in its proper perspective as a major phase in the turbulent history of East Asian peoples. In order to write *The Blue Wolf* (1960), a novelistic biography of Jenghis Khan, he had become thoroughly familiar with the major historical sources—*The Secret History of the Mongols* (1240), *Altan Tobchi* (completed around 1630), *The Original Source of the Mongols* (1661), and the memoirs of Jenghis's most trusted advisor, Yelü Ch'u-ts'ai, and of the Chinese Taoist Ch'ang-ch'un Chen-jen, who kept a record of his conversations with Jenghis Khan—as well as major studies by Western historians and chroniclers.

It was natural for Inoue, having completed *The Blue Wolf,* to focus his interest on Jenghis Khan's famous grandson, Kubilai. The Japanese long remembered the terrible Mongol invasions of the thirteenth century, and thanked their native gods for having interceded, twice sending *kamikaze* ("divine winds") to destroy the enemy fleets. They remembered the feared name Kubilai, but they knew nothing about the man. The Europeans came to know the historical Kubilai through Marco Polo's account of his sojourn at the court of the great Mongol khan; and, of course, a mythical Kubilai was created in Samuel Taylor Coleridge's romantic poem "Kubla Khan: Or a Vision in a Dream."

Because Kubilai is present throughout the story—sometimes directly involved in it, at other times dwelling in the thoughts of the principal Korean actors in the drama—a few Japanese critics have suggested that the author may have written this novel in order to describe the enigmatic character of that fabled khan, the dominant shaper of this historical drama. Indeed, as a means of attaining this presumed end, he may have selected Hong Tagu—a Korean by birth whom some of the Korean protagonists regard as Kubilai's alter ego —as the only other character who remains prominent throughout the story. Whereas Hong Tagu is portrayed consistently as a heartless opponent of Koryŏ, whether as a possible extension of Kubilai's will or because of his own hatred for people of his own race, the image of Kubilai in the minds of the Korean characters alternates, from one instance to the next, between that of an equally detestable opponent and that of a sympathetic anti-subject, a character who pursues his own ends but whose pursuit may, at times and perhaps unfortunately, conflict with the hopes and aspirations of the Koreans.

Nevertheless, the main characters whose thoughts and actions propel the narrative forward are the kings of Koryŏ, Wŏnjong and Ch'ungnyŏl, and their respective chief ministers, Yi Chang-yong and General Kim Pang-gyŏng. The image of Kubilai Khan in this novel is thus a composite of aspects of the character of Kubilai that have been gleaned from first-hand observations by the four Korean principals and the author's interpretation of those recorded facts.

The basic story of *Wind and Waves* is a series of historical events linked in precise chronological sequence. In writing this novel, Inoue read unusually ample historical documents—the *History of the Yuan (Mongol) Dynasty* (1370) and the *History of Koryŏ* (1451)—from which he drew liberally for facts and quotations. In particular, the contents, as well as the diction and tone, of the letters exchanged between Kubilai and the Korean kings and the memorials composed by Chief Minister Yi have served the author well as material for his portraits of those persons. It is worth noting that the quotations in Inoue's text appear in the original classical Chinese, a highly stylized, ornate language used by the Chinese and Koreans to compose official documents.

The discipline with which the author maintains the viewpoint of the people of Koryŏ is remarkable in a novel written by a Japanese. The Korean king, ordered to make certain that Mongol envoys are conducted safely to Japan, has to remind himself often of Kubilai's stern warning: "The fury of the wind and waves is a well-worn phrase; do not make it a pretext for shunning this duty." The island nation lying beyond the stormy strait is a mystery to the king, who knows nothing about Japan except what little his best-informed vassals have told him: that pine-covered hills rise steeply from its shores, against which the sea waves beat insistently, and that the rattle of warriors' swords and spears shatter the gentler sound of the sea winds passing through those forests of pines. The impressions are entirely Korean.

Bilingual Korean intellectuals today, surely the severest critics of any book about their own country, have been impressed with the historical authenticity of *Wind and Waves,* which recreates brilliantly the atmosphere of futility and despair that prevailed in Koryŏ during those decades of Mongol dominance. Although the principal observers are kings and ministers, the author seems to identify most closely with the general populace, who have tended to be neglected by present-day historians of Korea. Furthermore, the Japanese view of Korean history does not intrude here as it does even in recent histories of Korea written by native Korean scholars.

Wind and Waves reads like a thirteenth-century chronicle brought to life through spare narration, a minimum of dialogue, and slight yet

lucid characterization. Because it does not contain fanciful elabora-
tion, which many readers consider to be a necessary component of
historical novels, sophisticated Korean readers tend to regard *Wind
and Waves* as an artistic historical narrative. Perhaps for this reason, it
has been translated and published in Korea four times. Certainly the
author's compassion for human beings whose lives are controlled by
destiny or other forces beyond their control is as much in evidence
in this story as it is in his other works currently available in English
translation: *The Roof Tile of Tempyō, Tun-huang,* and *Lou-lan and
Other Stories.*

JAMES T. ARAKI

A NOTE ON
THE TRANSLATION

Because *Wind and Waves* is a story about four peoples, each using a different language, I have taken liberties in transcribing names and terms. I have avoided unusual phonetic symbols except for the diacritical mark which in Korean distinguishes important contrastive pairs of vowels: *o* and *ŏ*, *u* and *ŭ*. The Korean *o* is pronounced as in "go," and the *ŏ* as in "uh": thus, Koryŏ *(koryuh)*. The Korean *u* and *ŭ*, as in the name Punhŭi, are also contrastive vowels, *u* pronounced as in "rule," and *ŭ* as in "pull."

Personal names, except that of the author, have been given as they are in China, Korea, and Japan, with the surname first. The Asian lunar months, identified by number, have been given the names of the months in the solar calendar (the "first month" is January, the second is February, and so on), although in the cycle of seasons the first day of the first month would correspond more closely to a day in mid-February. Parenthetical matters appearing in this translation are also present in the Japanese original.

I thank Professor Peter H. Lee of the University of California, Los Angeles, for his help in transcribing Korean personal and geographic names.

WIND
and
WAVES

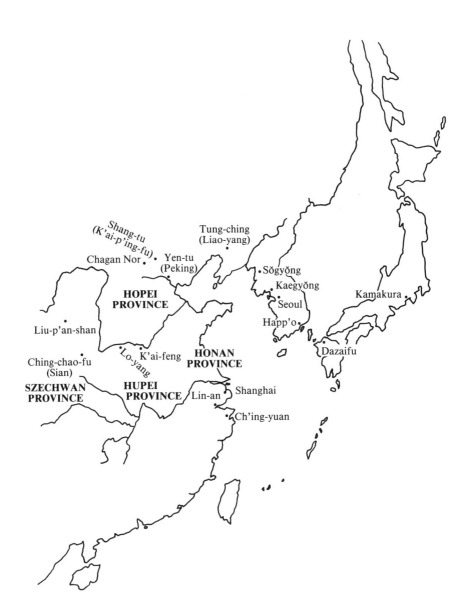

Shang-tu
(K'ai-p'ing-fu)
Chagan Nor
Yen-tu
(Peking)
Tung-ching
(Liao-yang)

HOPEI PROVINCE

Liu-p'an-shan

Sŏgyŏng
Kaegyŏng
Seoul
Kamakura
Happ'o

Ching-chao-fu
(Sian)
Lo-yang
K'ai-feng
HONAN PROVINCE

Dazaifu

SZECHWAN PROVINCE
HUPEI PROVINCE
Lin-an
Shanghai
Ch'ing-yuan

CHARACTERS

Chinese

Ch'en I. Sung Empire general; surrendered to the Mongols in 1276.

Fan Wen-hu. Sung Empire general; later, commander of the southern fleet in the 1281 invasion of Japan.

Hsia Kuei. Sung Empire general; surrendered to the Mongols in 1275.

Lu Wen-huan. Sung Empire general; surrendered to the Mongols in 1275.

Mongol and Tartar

Ahai. General in the army of occupation in Koryŏ, 1270.

Alahan. Joint commander with Fan Wen-hu of the southern fleet in the 1281 invasion of Japan.

Arigh-boge. Younger brother of Mongke and Kubilai.

Buha. Mongol magistrate; sent to Koryŏ to prosecute Yi Chang-yong in 1270.

Chang Kuo-kang. Senior *darughachi* assigned to Kaegyŏng in 1275.

Chang Shun-lung. A Moslem; served Princess Khutlgaimish as a *kelinkou*.

Chang To. Key member of the 1271 Mongol mission to Japan.

Chao Liang-pi. A Jurchen; Kubilai's ambassador to Japan in 1271 and again in 1272, staying in Dazaifu an entire year.

Che Hsin. A *kelinkou* in Princess Khutlgaimish's service; a Korean by birth.

Hindu. Colonial administrator of Koryŏ; supreme commander of the 1274 expedition against Japan; marshal in the 1281 expedition.

Ho Wen-chu. Envoy for the admonition of Japan in 1275; executed by the Japanese.

Ho-te. First Mongol envoy to be despatched to Japan, in 1266, and again in 1268.

1

Hua-teng. A Uighur by birth; member of the ill-fated 1275 Mongol mission to Japan.

Jenghis Khan. Founder of the Mongol Empire, known posthumously as T'ai-tzu (Great Founder) of the Yuan Dynasty of China.

Khutlgaimish. Kubilai's daughter; married King Ch'ungnyŏl of Koryŏ in 1274.

Kubilai. Succeeded his brother Mongke as Great Khan of the Mongols; known posthumously as Shih-tzu (Founding Emperor) of the Yuan Dynasty of China.

Kurimchi. Commander of the army escorting the Mongol ambassador to the port of embarkation in southern Koryŏ in 1271.

Liu Chieh. Same as above.

Mongke. Kubilai's predecessor as Great Khan of the Mongols; known posthumously as Emperor Hsien-tsung of the Yuan Dynasty.

Mongkut. Commander of the Mongol army of occupation in Koryŏ, 1270.

No Yong. Of Central Asian birth; served both Khutlgaimish and Koryŏ loyally.

Sartaq. Commander of the Mongol army of invasion in Koryŏ, 1232.

Saturjin. Member of the ill-fated 1275 Mongol mission to Japan; an Arab by birth.

Shih Shu. Colonial administrator assigned to Koryŏ in 1271.

Shih-mo T'ien-ch'ü. Assistant *darughachi* in Kaegyŏng, 1275.

Torenka. General in the Mongol army of occupation in Koryŏ, 1270.

Tu Shih-ch'ung. Envoy for the admonition of Japan, 1275; executed by the Japanese.

Wang Kuo-ch'ang. Mongol general; escorted the Mongol ambassador to the port of embarkation in southern Koryŏ in 1271.

Yelü Hsi-liang. Advisor to Kubilai; great grandson of Yelü Ch'u-ts'ai, senior advisor of Jenghis Khan.

Yesuder. Marshal of the Mongol army, 1259.

Yin-hou. A *kelinkou* in the service of Princess Khutlgaimish.

Yin-hung. Member of the first Mongol mission to Japan, 1266.

Korean

Chin Chahu. Accompanied the Mongol mission to Japan, 1268.

Cho I. Known as the first to describe Japan to Kubilai.

Cho Ingyu. Koryŏ's emissary to Kubilai in 1278.

Ch'oe T'an. Voluntarily ceded most of northern Koryŏ to Kubilai in 1271.

Chŏng Chayŏ. General who accompanied King Wŏnjong to Yen-tu in 1269.

Crown Prince Chŏn. Enthroned as King Wŏnjong in 1259.

Crown Prince Sim. King Wŏnjong's eldest son; enthroned as King Ch'ungnyŏl in 1274.

Crown Prince Wŏn. Son of King Ch'ungnyŏl and the Mongol princess Khutlgaimish; later became King Ch'ungsŏn.

Hong Nokchu. Minister active in the early 1270s.

Hong Pogwŏn. Traitor who led Mongol attacks against Koryŏ.

Hong Tagu. Son of Hong Pogwŏn; rose through the Mongol ranks to become senior military and civil administrator of expatriate Koreans, general in the 1274 invasion, supreme military commander in Koryŏ, marshal in the 1281 invasion.

Im Yŏn. Assassinated Marshal of the Army Kim Chun in 1268; temporarily banished King Wŏnjong in 1269.

Im Yumu. Im Yŏn's second son and heir.

In Kongsu. Oversaw Koryŏ during King Ch'ungnyŏl's absence in 1278.

Ki On. Escorted Princess Khutlgaimish to Koryŏ in 1274.

Kim Ch'an. Accompanied the 1266 Mongol mission to Japan.

Kim Chun. *See* Lord of Haeyang.

Kim Chujŏng. General in the 1281 invasion of Japan.

Kim Hŭn. Son of Kim Pang-gyŏng.

Kim Pang-gyŏng. Supreme military commander of Koryŏ; marshal, along with Hindu and Hong Tagu, during the 1281 Mongol invasion of Japan; succeeded Yi Chang-yong as chief minister.

Kim Poktae. General who served under Kim Pang-gyŏng; later slandered him.

Kim Posong. Hong Tagu's trusted Korean retainer.

Kim T'ongjŏng. Leader of the rebellious Sambyŏlch'o Elite Corps.

Kim Yusŏng. Koryŏ's envoy to Japan, 1270.

King Ch'ungnyŏl. Known earlier as Prince Sim; succeeded his father Wŏnjong in 1274.

King Kojong. Died in 1259; succeeded by his son Prince Chŏn.

King Wŏnjong. Known earlier as Prince Chŏn; succeeded his father, Kojong, in 1259.

Ko Yu. Koryŏ's envoy to Japan, 1270.

Kŭm Hun. King Wŏnjong's emissary to the Sambyŏlch'o Elite Corps in 1272.

Kwak Yŏp'il. Im Yŏn's emissary to the Mongols in 1270.

Lord of An'gyŏng Prince Ch'ang. Younger brother and confidant of King Wŏnjong; emissary to the Mongols in 1267.

Lord of Haeyang Kim Chun. Marshal of Koryŏ's army in the 1260s; assassinated by Im Yŏn.

Lord of Kwangpyŏng Prince Sun. Koryŏ's emissary to Kubilai, 1265.

Lord of Sin'an Prince Chŏn. Sent to the Mongols as hostage, 1239.

Lord of Sŭnghwa Prince On. Enthroned as king by rebels; executed in 1271.

Lord of Yongan Prince Hui. Emissary to Kubilai, 1260.

Lord of Yŏngnyŏng Prince Chun. Younger brother of the Lord of Sŭnghwa; sent to the Mongols as a hostage; later rose high in Mongol officialdom.

Na Yu. General despatched against the Sambyŏlch'o Elite Corps in 1272.

No Chinŭi. General who served under Kim Pang-gyŏng and later slandered him.

No Yŏnghŭi. An instigator of the 1270 rebellion.

Pae Chungson. Leader of the 1270 rebellion, in which he declared the lord of Sŭnghwa king of Koryŏ.

Pak Hŭisil. Army marshal sent to Mongke to sue for peace, 1258.

Pak Ku. General in the 1281 invasion of Japan.

Pak Ŭi. General who served as emissary to Kubilai in 1280.

Pak Yu. Chancellor of the treasury; recommended polygamy to help repopulate Koryŏ after the 1274 invasion of Japan.

Pan Pu. Koryŏ's envoy to Japan, 1267; accompanied the Mongol mission to Japan, 1268.

Prince Chong. King Wŏnjong's second son.

Prince Chun. *See* Lord of Yŏngnyŏng.

Queen Chŏngsin. King Ch'ungnyŏl's principal consort; renamed Chŏnghwa and forcibly separated from the king after his marriage to Khutlgaimish.

Queen Wŏnsŏng. The Korean title assumed by Kubilai's daughter, Khutlgaimish.

Shin Sajŏn. Accompanied the Mongol mission to Japan, 1268.

So Ch'an. Court interpreter; member of the ill-fated 1275 Mongol mission to Japan.

Sŏ Ch'o. Conducted the Mongol envoy Chao Liang-pi to Japan, 1271.

Song Kunbi. Accompanied the first Mongol mission to Japan, 1266.

Wi Tŭgyu. Marshal who served under Kim Pang-gyŏng and later slandered him.

Yi Chang-yong. Koryŏ's chief minister under King Wŏnjong; met several times with Kubilai.

Yi Punhŭi. Executed for treachery in 1278.

Yi Punsŏng. Yi Punhŭi's brother; executed for treachery in 1278.

Yi Ŭngnyŏl. Exiled in 1270 for opposing King Wŏnjong.

Yi Yŏnnyŏng. An accomplice of the rebel Ch'oe T'an.

Yu Kyŏng. Minister and elder statesman during the 1270s.

BOOK ONE

Yalu R.

P'o-so-fu

Ŭiju

Yongju   Pakchu

Ch'ŏlju

Chaju

Ch'ŏngch'ŏn R.

NORTHERN BORDER TERRITORY

Sŏgyŏng (P'yŏngyang)

Hamjong

Hwangju

Pongju

WESTERN SEAS TERRITORY

Haeju

Kaegyŏng

Paengnyŏng Is.

Taech'ŏng Is.

(Seoul)

Kanghwa Is.

Han R.

Ch'ŏngju

Andong

KYŎNGSANG PROVINCE

Kyŏngju

Chŏnju   Taegu

CHŎLLA PROVINCE

Kimju

Happ'o

Naju

Kŏje Is.

Hŭksan Is.

Tsushima

Chin Is.

Iki Is.

Dazaifu

Cheju Is.

CHAPTER 1

ON THE twenty-first of April in the year 1259, a ship carrying the crown prince of the kingdom of Koryŏ and a retinue of fewer than fifty men set sail from Kanghwa, an island off the western coast of the Korean peninsula. Some years earlier the royal court of Koryŏ had fled to that island seeking refuge from Mongol invaders—safe there because the Mongols feared the sea. Through surging coastal waters the ship headed for a point on the mainland not far from the abandoned capital, Kaegyŏng.

Crown Prince Chŏn was to deliver an instrument of surrender to the Mongols. Although propriety demanded that his father, King Kojong, present himself at the foreign court, and the Mongols were insisting on this point, the king, then sixty-eight, was so weakened by anguish over the prolonged war and by the ravages of old age that he now lay in a sickbed, to all eyes stricken with a mortal illness. The crown prince would have to represent his father.

No year went by without the Mongols overrunning the area about Kaegyŏng and then advancing upon a vantage point that overlooked Kanghwa Island. From atop Mount Munsu, which rose above the narrow channel, they flaunted their banners to proclaim their mastery over Koryŏ.

On the shore an escort of Mongol troops waited to greet them. They traveled northward over devastated land, their mounts sometimes knee-deep in the quagmire. The fields lay barren, and no smoke rose from the houses. Even a lone Mongol cavalryman sent the people fleeing to the hills or offshore islands. The villages were now deserted.

The travelers arrived at Kaegyŏng (present-day Kaesŏng) at dusk.

9

Although the people called it the "former capital," it was still the national capital of Koryŏ. Kanghwa Island was only a temporary refuge.

The Mongol presence in Kaegyŏng was overwhelming. The palace, monasteries, and residences were billets for Mongol soldiers. Stables had been built at every well. Beyond the city walls, campsites for the horde stretched out across the plains. The prince had lived in the palace in Kaegyŏng until he was fourteen. What he saw reminded him once again that Mongol horsemen had been trampling his people into submission for nearly three decades. Only the golden forsythia blooming beside occasional ramshackle dwellings seemed to have endured unchanged.

The travelers were detained in Kaegyŏng for three days, then resumed their journey northward. Some days they were forced to travel all through the day and most of the night; some days they were detained for long hours at nameless villages. In early May they crossed the Taedong River and arrived at Sŏgyŏng, the "western capital" (present-day P'yŏngyang), now a thriving city under Mongol occupation. The garrison was made up of men of many races— Khitans and Jurchens and Koreans who had become Mongol subjects. The same blend of races inhabited the city. The streets of Sŏgyŏng resounded with the din of merchants' cries, and shrill Korean could be heard mingling with exotic accents from unknown countries.

The party traveled on through Ŭiju, then crossed the Yalu River. Beyond lay a wholly unfamiliar land. The days now were as searing as any in midsummer in Koryŏ, but the light chill of the mornings and evenings reminded them of autumn in their homeland. Although Prince Chŏn was traveling to the court of Mongke, the great khan of the Mongols, he did not know if his destination was Karakorum, the Tartar capital, or farther south in China where Mongke had sent his hordes to conquer the Sung Empire. Nor did his escort seem to know, for he was given revised orders at posts along the route of travel.

When they came to the Hu River, they saw the current swollen by heavy rain. Yi Sejae, a high retainer, advised the crown prince to wait until the flow subsided. But Prince Chŏn, prodded by anxiety, insisted on crossing the river and the Mongol commander consented. On May 18 they arrived in Tung-ching (present-day Liao-yang). Within the city walls of Tung-ching they saw a massive army which, they were told, would leave for Koryŏ the next day. The crown prince immediately sent emissaries to Yesuder, marshal of the army, bearing gifts of fruits, wine, fifty *kŭn* of silver, and a wine casket and a jar fashioned from silver. The next morning Prince Chŏn met with Marshal Yesuder, a large, heavily bearded man.

"Emperor Mongke has joined his armies in the war against the Sung Empire," the marshal said. "I have been assigned the task of subjugating Koryŏ and have ordered my army to march into your country. What has brought you here?"

Prince Chŏn replied, "My country has been so weakened that it cannot sustain itself without the benevolence of His Majesty the emperor and your goodwill, honored marshal. I have traveled far in order to be received in audience by His Imperial Majesty and pledge fealty to him. I ask you not to send your army into my country."

"I have a question to ask you—only one," Yesuder said. "Has the royal court of Koryŏ left Kangdo, or has it not?" Kangdo, the "capital beyond the sea," was the small royal city on Kanghwa Island. The royal court of Koryŏ had to leave Kangdo—this was the ultimate demand, made over the years by the invading Mongols at every negotiation.

"The people have already left the island, and the royal court will probably move to a new site whenever the emperor commands it," Prince Chŏn said, wishing to mollify him. But Yesuder replied that he had no choice but to attack if the court remained on the island.

"You, marshal, once said to us, 'I shall call off the invasion if Koryŏ's crown prince comes to pay us homage.' That is why I have come to your country. If you should lead your army into Koryŏ now, you will terrify my people and they will scurry into hiding. Never again will they heed your appeals. Can we believe what you told us, or can we not?"

Trapped by Chŏn's logic, Yesuder rescinded his orders and instead despatched a small contingent of troops to demolish the walls of Kangdo.

The travelers left Tung-ching the next day. Their journey took

them across barren plains, then over a stretch of mountainous country, and at last they crossed the Great Wall and arrived at Yen-ching
(present-day Peking). But they did not go into the city. Having
lodged the night outside the city walls, they found themselves again
on the road of travel, crossing a flat plain that seemed to stretch on
endlessly. More than ten days later, their path led them onto a broad
plateau. The landscape changed gradually to one of undulating hills,
and soon they were riding along the skirts of tall mountains that
receded layer upon layer into the distance.

When the party crossed the turgid flow of the Yellow River and
arrived in Lo-yang, Prince Chŏn was informed that Mongke would
soon leave the battlefields in Szechwan province for his summer palace in the north. The party would follow the south shore of the
great river to Ching-chao-fu (Sian), then travel westward to Liu-
p'an-shan (in Lung-te prefecture, Kansu province), where Jenghis
Khan, the first monarch of the Mongol Empire, was known to have
died. There the prince would present the instrument of surrender to
the Mongol emperor.

In early September, more than four months after leaving Kangdo,
the crown prince of Koryŏ and his retinue arrived in Liu-p'an-shan
and, for the first time since crossing the Yalu River, were given respite from the wearisome swaying to the constant motion of their
mounts. Liu-p'an-shan, a small city at the foot of the mountain that
was its namesake, was congested with soldiers and horses, but Prince
Chŏn sensed a strangeness the moment his party entered the city. A
ban had been proclaimed on all carousing. Military movements had
ceased altogether, and the troops garrisoned in the city lacked the
boisterousness that had been displayed in every city he had passed
through. The soldiers did not know the reason for this somberness;
they had merely been told that an extraordinary event had taken
place.

Mongke had been leading his troops in battle against the Sung
Empire since the previous winter. This year his armies had advanced
on the city of Ho-chou and now had it surrounded, but the
emperor was stricken by illness at Tiao-yü-shan in Ho-chou (Ho-
ch'uan city in Szechwan province), not far from the battlefields.

Prince Chŏn learned of Mongke's death five days after arriving in

Liu-p'an-shan. He lingered in Liu-p'an-shan for a month, then retraced his recent route of travel back toward Honan, south of the Yellow River, hoping to encounter Kubilai, brother and logical successor of the late Mongol emperor. Kubilai was expected to suspend his campaign in the Hupei region and return north, and both Prince Chŏn and his Mongol escort hoped they could meet him as he traveled back to the Mongol capital.

They dawdled for several days at Ching-chao-fu and again at T'ung-kuan because they were told that Kubilai had not yet disengaged his troops from battle in Hupei. Eventually they arrived back in Lo-yang and spent more than a month in the ancient capital. It was the season for chrysanthemums. The flowers, predominantly yellows and whites, grew in wild profusion in every garden, and their delicate fragrance pervaded the city.

Toward the end of November, there was a rumor that Kubilai had at last decided to withdraw his armies from Hupei. Prince Chŏn's party left promptly for K'ai-feng, which was on the route of Kubilai's northerly march. At a small village, with K'ai-feng still two days' journey ahead of them, they encountered Kubilai's army. It was a massive army such as the Korean crown prince could never have imagined. Countless units passed through the village in an unending stream through most of the day. At last Kubilai's carriage was seen approaching in the distance. Standing at the village entrance to greet the renowned brother of the late emperor, Crown Prince Chŏn wore a wide-sleeved purple robe of sheer silk, girded with a belt of rhinoceros leather, and a soft-pointed silk cap; he carried an ivory scepter in one hand and held a standard upright with the other. His vassals were also attired in ceremonial finery. Kubilai, who had been informed of the presence of the crown prince of Koryŏ, stopped at the village with a contingent of troops and met with Prince Chŏn in a small garden next to a farmhouse.

Kubilai, then forty-five years of age, wore a tight-fitting suit of armor over his ample body. His face was full, and his complexion was unusually fair for a Mongol. His black beard contained a few golden strands, his large almond-shaped eyes were dark and direct, but his gaze was softened by a suggestion of a smile.

Although the air was frigid, the wan sunlight of early winter shed warmth on the men. When Prince Chŏn presented Kubilai with the instrument of surrender on behalf of his royal father, Kubilai responded with undisguised pleasure and thanked the crown prince for having traveled such a great distance to pay his nation homage.

"Koryŏ is a nation a thousand leagues distant," Kubilai continued. "Emperor T'ai-tsung of the T'ang Dynasty led an army of conquest into your country in an attempt to subjugate it, but he failed. In the six centuries since then, Koryŏ could not be brought to submission however mighty the armies that were sent against it. Today the scion of Koryŏ's royal house has come to pledge fealty to my nation, as Heaven has surely willed it. We have fought each other, but that time is now part of the past. Surely our two nations will be joined in friendship and abide in peace as members of one family in the years to come."

The warmth of Kubilai's words touched Chŏn to the core. He knew that Mongke's successor would be elected at the Kuriltai, the great gathering of all the Tartar princes and generals; he would pray for the selection of this stalwart, yet gentle and compassionate prince, surely a man of surpassing wisdom.

They would meet again in Yen-ching, Kubilai said at the conclusion of their brief meeting. Then he left the village to resume his northerly march. Prince Chŏn remained rapt in a state of wonderment. A man who seemed to be the very opposite of his preconception of Mongol khans would very likely succeed the diabolic Mongke as the supreme Mongol leader. Because Chŏn had felt only hatred for Mongols, he was surprised that his feelings toward them were now mixed with ambiguity.

Prince Chŏn's party followed Kubilai's army northward. Already at the Yellow River crossing they had fallen somewhat behind, and soon the distance separating them was considerable. Kubilai's huge army marched across the plains of Hopei so rapidly as to astound the Koreans. Chŏn's party arrived in Yen-ching in early December, two weeks after Kubilai's army.

In Yen-ching the crown prince of Koryŏ was kept in idleness. He received no orders or instructions. No one important came to see him. Kubilai was known to be in Yen-ching but he sent no word.

Chŏn's place of lodging was changed several times in accordance with directives issued by the authorities. Those directives, at the least, assured the crown prince that his presence had not been forgotten by the Mongol high command.

The new year of 1260 arrived. It snowed continually and the intense cold prevented Chŏn from venturing out of doors. He grew restless, confined day after day in cramped quarters. He heard rumors of dissension within the Tartar ranks over the choice of the next great khan. One of Mongke's brothers, Arigh-boge, had stayed in Karakorum during Mongke's campaign in south China and had proclaimed himself great khan upon the death of his brother; his precipitous act had aroused Kubilai's wrath. Among Mongke's brothers Kubilai was the eldest. The Tartar princes and generals were preoccupied with the question of imperial succession, and the crown prince of Koryŏ was far removed from their thoughts.

One day in mid-February, a messenger sent by Kubilai informed Prince Chŏn of the death of his father, King Kojong. The messenger was a seventeen-year-old youth named Hong Tagu. Chŏn remembered that Hong Tagu, slender-faced with well-placed features, had been in close attendance upon Kubilai when they had met the year before in a village south of K'ai-feng. Prince Chŏn was oddly fascinated by this youth, unmistakably a Korean by birth. With his cold eyes, a broad forehead that suggested a maturity beyond his years, thin-lobed ears, and colorless lips, he struck the crown prince as an emotionless, calculating sort who was not to be trusted. Quite as if to confirm Prince Chŏn's impression of him, Hong Tagu assumed the role of a harbinger of bane. Pridefully erect, he brought himself face to face with the crown prince.

"I represent the supreme Mongol authority," he said in a low voice. "My name is Hong Tagu."

The imperious tone of his remark conveyed an attitude—he was Kubilai's surrogate, and he expected the crown prince to assume a posture of humility. Chŏn bowed low. He heard Hong Tagu address him in a dispassionate monotone.

"I regret to bring grievous news to you, crown prince of Koryŏ. On the thirtieth of June last year, your royal father Kojong passed away in Kangdo. I have just received this sad report, and bring you my deep-felt condolence. I have been told that your son now rules in your place, and I trust that you will find this news reassuring."

No sooner had Hong Tagu finished than he turned and left as impersonally as he had come. Prince Chŏn was not surprised by the news of his father's death; he had been prepared for it. But he puzzled over the fact that the Mongols had not learned about it until nearly eight months later. Perhaps his government had chosen to keep the mourning secret until he returned, but had ultimately announced the king's death because his return to Koryŏ had been greatly delayed. The crown prince's concern for the state of his country in the wake of the king's death was mitigated by the knowledge that his eldest son, twenty-four-year-old Prince Sim, was at the helm of state. He was himself powerless, being in a remote land, but he was comforted when he recalled Sim's aristocratic visage and his unusually thoughtful, discreet nature.

Prince Chŏn and his vassals spent three days praying on behalf of their departed king. When they emerged from their mourning, they were met by a messenger whose arrival at that precise moment bespoke Kubilai's wish to invite the crown prince to his palace at the earliest opportunity. Prince Chŏn's meeting with Kubilai this time would be a formal audience in which the representative of Mongol authority would receive the crown prince of Koryŏ, who had come to pledge fealty.

Prince Chŏn was led to a stately room in the inner recesses of the palace; there he was received by Kubilai, attired in dazzling resplendence. Kubilai first spoke consolingly of the death of King Kojong, then explained that his preoccupation with the affairs of the Mongol Empire had prevented him from extending appropriate courtesies to the crown prince, who had come from afar and had abided since the past year in a country in which he was a guest.

During the ensuing banquet, musicians played exotic instruments and Chŏn heard Kubilai's deep, resonant voice against an unbroken background of pleasant strains: "You will become king of Koryŏ when you return to your country. Here the election of the great khan of the Mongols will take place before long. Perhaps both the Mongol and Koryŏ nations will begin anew together under new rulers. The former monarchs, who had long been mortal enemies, died within a few months of each other. It may have been their karma. The long years of war have come to an end, and I foresee a new era in which our nations shall exist by helping each other. We shall deliver appropriate counsel to your country immediately upon the accession of our next emperor. Although I should be pleased to have you remain with us, you are needed in your own country. Feel free to make your departure as soon as the weather becomes agreeable for travel."

Although Prince Chŏn still lingered in a state of grief, at that moment he experienced the wonderment he had felt after his earlier meeting with Kubilai. Perhaps, he thought, Koryŏ would never again know the dread of having its land trampled underfoot by nightmarish Mongol horsemen.

Prince Chŏn wished to leave Yen-ching right away, but the heavy snowfall discouraged him from immediate travel. Following his audience with Kubilai, he noticed that his Mongol hosts attended him with solicitude rather than indifference. He was given lodging within the palace, and was attended closely by many court ladies and servants. His meals were now more sumptuous than any he had been served before.

With fair weather finally prevailing, Prince Chŏn left Yen-ching on February 25. He was escorted by a contingent of Mongol guards carrying the ensign of Koryŏ at the head of their column. Kubilai also left Yen-ching that day for K'ai-p'ing-fu, the site of the Kuriltai where the next great khan would be elected. The two parties left by the same city gate but took to roads leading in opposite directions.

The crown prince was in a hurry to get home. He subjected himself to unbroken travel, often moving continuously through the day and night. In early March he crossed the frozen surface of the Yalu River and was once again in his own country. He saw a ravaged land, its once fertile fields reduced to barren wastes. The travelers braved snow daily as they crossed the inhospitable plain, and on March 20 they arrived at Kangdo. Although Prince Chŏn's grief over his father's death revived with a new intensity, he felt a glimmer of hope penetrating his melancholy. Soon it would be spring. The snow would vanish and the trees would bring forth new buds.

*

On the ninth of April, a state paper from the Mongol court was delivered to the court of Koryŏ. King Kojong had earlier despatched Marshal Pak Hŭisil to the Mongols with several demands to be negotiated as conditions for surrender; but Mongke had sent him an equivocal reply. This paper, however, touched specifically on each of the requests, and granted most of them. It stated, in effect, that all Mongol military units would be withdrawn from Koryŏ; that all Koreans, both captives and fugitives, would be examined and released upon their pledging allegiance to the Mongol Empire; that the Mongol soldiers found guilty of pillaging during the withdrawal would be executed. Such generosity was surely due to Kubilai's intercession.

On April 21, Chŏn ascended to the throne to become King Wŏnjong of Koryŏ. Sim, who had overseen the nation during his father's absence, was invested as crown prince. A month earlier in Mongolia, Kubilai had been elected great khan. The news of Kubilai's enthronement as *shih-tzu*, "founding emperor," of the Mongol dynasty reached the new monarch of Koryŏ on April 29.

King Wŏnjong promptly appointed his uncle, the lord of Yongan Prince Hui, as the emissary to be despatched that very day to congratulate the new emperor of the Mongols. Even though he was aware that such haste might violate diplomatic protocol, he could not contain his wish to express his joy at once. He concluded his message with this statement of gratitude:

> I have been deeply moved by your kindness, which is not less than that which the beloved youngest child of a family inspires in loving parents. I have assumed a debt of gratitude of which I am constantly reminded. It is a debt which I and my descendants shall honor with our lives.

The king received three letters from Kubilai in close succession. The first, received in Kangdo on August 18, read in part as follows:

> Retain your nation's traditions and customs with regard to clothing and headdress. Travel from my country to yours shall be restricted to

those carrying proper credentials. You shall move your royal court back to the capital, Kaegyŏng, as expeditiously as conditions permit. Our garrisons shall be withdrawn in autumn. I shall abide by the laws that govern my entire realm, and I shall value sincerity above all. Understand my intent well lest you succumb to the temptations of doubt and fear.

Recalling the cruelty of the previous demands made by the Mongols, King Wŏnjong could scarcely believe the magnanimity conveyed in Kubilai's letter. Mongol troops would be withdrawn in the autumn, never again to reappear in his land! And although the moving of the court—a long-standing demand of the Mongols—was to be accomplished quickly, it was to be done, in Kubilai's words, "as expeditiously as conditions permit." Having read the letter, Wŏnjong repaired to his chamber and wept. He wept for a long while, overwhelmed by the sorrow he felt for his father, King Kojong, who had known only torment and had not lived to see the changes brought about by the new Mongol emperor.

*

Koryŏ dwelt in a nightmare that had begun thirty years earlier, during the reign of Ogodei, successor of Jenghis Khan. Jenghis, born around the year 1167, rose from leader of a tribe by the Onon River to become great khan of all the Tartarian hordes; he warred against the Chin Empire to bring the vastness north of the Yellow River under his rule; he conquered the Western Liang and then invaded the Khorazm Empire east of the Caspian Sea to assert his authority over central Asia; he then sent his armies eastward to destroy the Tanguts of the empire of Western Hsia; but on the last of his several assaults on the resurgent Chin Empire he was felled by sickness at Liu-p'an-shan in Kansu province.

In 1229, two years after Jenghis's death, Ogodei became great khan. Although he reigned but thirteen years, he accomplished what Jenghis had left unfinished, the destruction of the Chin Empire; then he launched the war against the Sung Empire of China. While attacking the Sung, he sent units into Liaotung Peninsula against the remnants of the Chin army. As soon as the Chin holdouts were pacified, he redirected those units to the Korean peninsula to begin an invasion of Koryŏ, a nation which at one time had sent Jenghis Khan tributary goods as an expression of deference, not of fear.

In the third year of Ogodei's reign, a Mongol army under the command of Sartaq appeared on the northern border of the peninsular nation, its intent of conquest undisguised. Through that autumn and winter, more than a dozen walled cities in the northwest fell to Sartaq, and the Korean army sent north to repel the Mongols met with inglorious defeat at Anju. Three of Sartaq's divisions besieged the capital city, Kaegyŏng, demanding capitulation. That year, 1231, was Kojong's eighteenth as Koryŏ's king; Crown Prince Chŏn had just turned thirteen. Compelled to submit, Koryŏ presented the Mongols with large amounts of gold and tributary goods; Koryŏ also bowed to the Mongol insistence on stationing *darughachi* in fourteen walled cities north of Sŏgyŏng. As the resident commissioner who supervised civil administration in an occupied territory, the *darughachi* was in effect the supreme authority in any area under Mongol occupation.

Sartaq spent the remainder of that year on the peninsula and left in the spring of the following year, 1232, having posted seventy-two *darughachi* in Kaegyŏng and lesser administrative districts. Upon returning to Liaotung, he assigned a supreme *darughachi* to Kaegyŏng to oversee all internal affairs of Koryŏ; the man he sent was a Khitan named Tu-tan. Soon after his arrival in Koryŏ's capital, Tu-tan demanded one thousand otter pelts as tribute and, as hostages, many skilled artisans and five hundred girls from the royal house and families of high-ranking officials. King Kojong despatched an emissary to Liaotung, bearing the otter pelts but imploring Sartaq to retract his demand for hostages. Sartaq, angered, banished the unlucky emissary to the wilderness of the Mongolian desert.

Unable to endure such punitive exactions, the king and ministers of Koryŏ determined to rise up against their oppressors. They moved the royal court from Kaegyŏng to Kanghwa Island and ordered the people to flee to the mountains and the countless tiny islands dotting the coastal waters. The Koryŏ army then attacked the Mongol *darughachi* in the walled cities in the northern half of the peninsula.

That autumn, Sartaq crossed the northern border into Koryŏ at the head of a gigantic army, and sent an emissary to Kanghwa Island demanding that King Kojong return to the mainland. Kanghwa Island, ringed with precipitous mountains, was an impregnable fortress inaccessible to the Mongols, who had no knowledge of naval warfare. King Kojong refused. Sartaq thereupon led his army southward, beyond Kaegyŏng to the Hanyang Mountain Fortress (within the area known today as Seoul), which he captured, and was at the city walls of Yongin when he was struck by an arrow from the bow of a Buddhist monk. During that campaign the treasured woodblocks for printing the compendium of sacred Buddhist scriptures, the *Tripitaka*, were destroyed. Those many thousands of woodblocks, stored at Puin Monastery on Mount P'algong, northeast of Taegu, were put to the torch by Mongol troops who had crossed the Sobaek Mountains to devastate the southeastern region of the peninsula.

The leaderless Mongol army withdrew across the border. But in 1235 it returned with a vengeance, led by Marshal Tanqut. Intent only on ravaging the peninsula, Tanqut made no attempt to negotiate peace with the royal court on Kanghwa Island. The depredation continued for six years. The famed pagoda of the Hwangnyong Monastery in Kyŏngju was among the many cultural treasures reduced to ashes by Tanqut's predatory army.

Seeing his country brutally devastated, King Kojong devised a plan to obtain relief, however temporary. In October of 1239 he despatched the lord of Sin'an Prince Chŏn and nine other young males of royal lineage to the Mongol court in a gesture of submission; and in 1241 he sent another hostage, the royal prince Chun, the lord of Yŏngnyŏng. However, when Guyuk succeeded Ogodei on the Mongol throne in July of 1246, he promptly ordered Marshal A-mu-k'an to resume the war, for the reason that the king of Koryŏ had not left Kanghwa Island.

Mongke ascended to the throne following Guyuk's death three years later. Mongke also demanded that the royal court of Koryŏ leave Kanghwa Island and return to Kaegyŏng. When the Korean king refused, he placed the Mongol prince Yeku at the head of a large army that swept across the border into the peninsula. King Kojong negotiated for the withdrawal of the Mongols and, as soon as the invaders were gone, sent his younger brother, the lord of An'gyŏng Prince Ch'ang, to deliver felicitations to the Mongol court.

Mongke was displeased by what he considered to be a meager gesture of submission—one prince was not enough. In 1254 he appointed Jalairtai as marshal of the Army for the Subjugation of the East and ordered him to bring Koryŏ to its knees. The *History of Koryŏ* describes thus the consequences of the hostilities in the year Jalairtai first appeared on the Korean peninsula:

> That year the Mongol troops took captive more than 206,800 of our men and women; the number of our people they slaughtered was beyond reckoning. Every city and county that lay in the path of their march was reduced to ashes. Never before in the history of Mongol invasions had our country been so devastated.

The Koreans could not have dreamt that even greater devastation would follow. The invaders made a custom of sweeping across the country every year in autumn, harvesting all the grain and plundering every city in the path of their march. They usually killed everyone who resisted before finally withdrawing with a large number of captive men and women. Whenever the Mongols came, the Koreans survived only by abandoning the cities and fleeing to the mountains and coastal islands.

In 1257 King Kojong decided to submit to the Mongols—he would leave his island stronghold and surrender. Again he despatched his younger brother, the lord of An'gyŏng Prince Ch'ang, to the Mongol court to negotiate the terms of surrender. Prince Ch'ang left Kangdo in December. A year later, in December of 1258, the king sent Marshal Pak Hŭisil to resume the negotiations that had been initiated by Prince Ch'ang. In that year's interval, the royal court in Kangdo had seethed with a violent conflict between the peace and war factions. The militant Ch'oe clan, which had dominated court politics, fell from power in the aftermath of the turbulence. With the Ch'oe eliminated, King Kojong was able to assert his authority to implement his policy of capitulation. It was then, in 1259, that Crown Prince Chŏn was appointed envoy to deliver the instrument of surrender to the Mongol court.

Two months after the crown prince left Kangdo, Mongol troops came to Kanghwa Island and began promptly to demolish the fortification. Those sections of the walls most crucial to the defense of Kangdo were torn down by Korean laborers conscripted by the Mongols. Toiling under the hot sun of early summer, they destroyed great lengths of the outer wall as well as sections of other walls that formed the intermediate and inner perimeters of defense. King Kojong died on the night of June 30, and was therefore spared the agony of witnessing the dismantling of his island fortress. The last thirty years of Kojong's life had coincided with the era of Mongol depredation of the Korean peninsula. In those three decades he had not known a single carefree day.

*

The letter which the new Mongol emperor sent to the newly enthroned monarch of Koryŏ contained no falsehood. All of its provisions were carried out. Captives and fugitives from Koryŏ were freed soon after the issuance of an imperial edict ordering their release. More than one hundred forty families that had settled in Mongol territory were repatriated to Koryŏ. The lord of Yongan Prince Hui, who had been sent to congratulate Kubilai on his accession to the Mongol throne, returned to Kangdo in August and informed the king that he had observed the orderly withdrawal of Mongol troops as he passed through Sŏgyŏng.

King Wŏnjong continued to reside in Kangdo. The former capital still lay in ruins. The palace had been used as billets for Mongol troops and in its dilapidated state was unfit for royalty. A new palace would have to be built.

The reconstruction of Kaegyŏng was begun in the spring of 1261, the second year of King Wŏnjong's reign, and it was now late summer. The rate of progress had been agonizingly slow. The great thoroughfare of the partially completed capital was strewn with corpses of people who had starved to death, and the boulevards and streets were now the province of beggars and thieves. The Mongol general Shultai, *darughachi* of Kaegyŏng, had been in charge of the reconstruction of the palace. He had conscripted thousands of laborers and driven them harshly, day and night. When he was abruptly recalled to his country, the laborers vanished from Kaegyŏng; their immediate concern was to accumulate enough food to survive a bleak winter. When Shultai left, Koryŏ for the first time in thirty years was wholly free of Mongol constraint.

The king intended to move his court back to Kaegyŏng when the city was rebuilt. The phrase "as conditions permit" in Kubilai's letter suggested that he might tolerate a brief delay. Although the king was mindful of the urgency, he was preoccupied with problems that demanded immediate solution: fields and forests throughout the land lay desolate; broken embankments could not contain the flood of coming rains; most of his people had lost their dwellings, and winter was fast approaching; many would freeze to death or die of starvation.

An edict from Kubilai received in October ordered the Koryŏ government to draw up population registers; this was in anticipation of the levying of Koreans to serve as soldiers and as laborers to transport foodstuffs and maintain stored provisions. If the people of Koryŏ should be called upon to serve the Mongol military, such registers would facilitate their prompt conscription. In the spring of the following year, 1262, another edict was received, specifying tributary goods to be submitted to the Mongols. The Koryŏ government sent every solicited item except baby sparrow hawks, which could not be found at that time of year. Six months later, an emissary sent by Kubilai accused Koryŏ of laggardness in failing to provide the sparrow hawks and, at the same time, stipulated a new levy of twenty thousand *kŭn* of "fine copper."

No one at the court of Koryŏ knew what "fine copper" was— only by asking the Mongol emissary did they learn that it was the Mongol term for brass. King Wŏnjong promptly sent an emissary to Kubilai with twenty baby sparrow hawks and six hundred twelve *kŭn* of brass appropriated from his courtiers. He begged forgiveness for the delay in delivering the sparrow hawks. Brass, he explained, was not produced in areas south of the Yalu River; every bit of brass in Koryŏ had been obtained from Chinese merchants, and twenty thousand *kŭn* was an undreamt of quantity in Koryŏ. Although he was pained by his inability to comply with the imperial command, he begged that the six hundred twelve *kŭn* be accepted as a reasonable offering.

Kubilai's reply was immediate. It stated, in effect: I have granted your every wish; I have not imposed Mongol customs on your people, and instead have decreed that your people retain their own customs in matters of apparel and headdress; I have withdrawn all Mongol troops, freed Korean captives, and enabled those who had fled to the coastal islands to return; but you have shown no eagerness to comply with my wish for rare fowl and have responded to my levy of a trivial amount of brass with an unconvincing excuse; if you cannot comply with orders pertaining to trifles, how can you then be trusted with matters of importance; the Mongol Empire has strict ordinances governing tributary states and you must abide by them; you must present hostages, organize your people into a comprehensive network for the relaying of information, and have them in readiness to gather and transport food and supplies in times of war; never must you be remiss in forwarding the annual tribute; you sent us the lord of Yŏngnyŏng Prince Chun as hostage but have failed to fulfill your other obligations; attend to these matters at once.

King Wŏnjong replied quickly, stating that he would fulfill Kubilai's every wish. He refrained from mentioning the registry of the populace for eventual conscription. Nor did he touch upon the matter of relocating the royal court. His country continued to suffer from severe deprivation, and more and more of his people were drifting into vagrancy. Koryŏ could not possibly organize itself in such ways as to satisfy Kubilai.

The king's emissary returned empty-handed, for Kubilai was displeased and refused to issue a reply. King Wŏnjong quickly sent a second letter in which he described the conditions in Koryŏ in fine detail and begged Kubilai to defer his demand for tribute. He felt certain that Kubilai would be sympathetic. Whereas most of his courtiers tended to regard Kubilai as a Mongol khan no different from his predecessors, King Wŏnjong remembered how he had been spellbound by his warmth. He was not disappointed, for Kubilai sent him this charitable reply:

> Because I was concerned with trivialities, I failed to discern your sincerity and therefore accused you of laggardness. You have written me again, asking that I defer your compliance until your people have had the opportunity to recover from their deprivation. Your conviction and honesty are consistent with just principles, and I grant your wish. Your people have many needs, and you may decide which of their needs are to be met.

Two years passed. The next letter from Kubilai to Wŏnjong was received in 1264. It stated, in effect: Now, in the fifth year of my reign, the rebellion of Arigh-boge having been quelled, I shall summon all the kings and princes who are my subjects to an assembly at my court in Shang-tu (K'ai-p'ing); you shall, of course, attend and perform the customary ritual of homage.

Never in the history of Koryŏ had its reigning king traveled beyond the nation's border to pay homage to a foreign monarch. Moreover, the Mongol intent was suspect, and many doubted the wisdom of complying with Kubilai's command. But urged by the chief minister Yi Chang-yong, the king ultimately decided to present himself at the Mongol court.

King Wŏnjong left Kangdo on August 12, and on October 1, in the palatial setting of Yen-tu, he was received in audience by Kubilai, now his suzerain. The city of Yen-ching had been renamed Yen-tu following Kubilai's accession to the throne, and a palace had been built there, as well as another in Shang-tu, the western capital. The heads of tributary states had first been summoned to Shang-tu, but the Mongol emperor had changed his mind and convened his subjects in Yen-tu.

Kubilai, speaking benignly as he had on their two previous meetings, asked Wŏnjong many questions concerning Koryŏ's recovery from the devastation inflicted by the Mongol invaders. He also asked about Koryŏ's standing army, which, the lord of Yŏngnyŏng Prince Chun had told him, numbered fifty thousand troops. Ten thousand, he said, should be sufficient for the defense of the homeland; the other forty thousand should be garrisoned in Mongol territory. Appalled by Chun's exaggeration, Wŏnjong hastened to explain that Koryŏ's army had been reduced to fewer than five thousand troops. Kubilai listened quietly, inclined his head in a gesture of acknowledgment, and did not press his demand. Wŏnjong sighed in relief as he withdrew from the imperial presence.

On the eighteenth, Wŏnjong presented himself at the Mount Wan-shou palace to take his leave of Kubilai, who wished him well and favored him with a parting gift of ten camels. In late December, he arrived without incident at Kangdo, accompanied by those curious beasts which could not be put to any use in his country.

With the coming of the new year, King Wŏnjong sent the lord of Kwangp'yŏng Prince Sun to the Mongol court to deliver the customary felicitations. Prince Sun returned in early summer and, at an assemblage of the royal family and principal courtiers at Kangdo, reported that the emperor had inquired solicitously about their kingdom. Consoled by Kubilai's message, many members of the court began to regard Kubilai as a man quite different from the tyrant of their imagination, and for the first time in the history of Koryŏ, they expressed praise for a Mongol khan. A few even dared to rejoice. In the deliberations that followed, everyone agreed that the royal court must be moved back to Kaegyŏng, and a registry of Koryŏ's populace drawn up as soon as possible. But no one suggested how this could be done. Instead they talked about the scarcity of food. Koryŏ had suffered a disastrous famine the year before, and its effects were now being felt. How to keep the people alive until the next harvest—this was their most pressing problem. Although the Mongols had left five years earlier, three decades of continual depredation had left Koryŏ badly wounded.

The rebuilding of Kaegyŏng had been suspended. Yet its population continued to grow, for in its unfinished state it conveniently accommodated an ever-increasing number of vagrants.

CHAPTER 2

IN OCTOBER of 1266, this message came from Kubilai, borne to the king by two Mongol vice ministers:

> Recently your countryman Cho I informed me that Japan lies in close proximity to Koryŏ, that its institutions and government are praiseworthy, and that it has sent envoys to China since the eras of the Han [202 B.C.–A.D. 220] and T'ang [618–907] dynasties. I am therefore despatching Ho-te and others to Japan to establish a relationship of reciprocity. You are to provide guides who shall conduct my envoys to Japan so that they may enlighten the Japanese and persuade them to comply with my wishes and accept our rightful ways. I am pleased to entrust Your Highness with the responsibility for the success of this mission. "The fury of the wind and waves" is a well-worn phrase; do not use it as a pretext for shunning this duty. You might claim that you have not yet established amity with Japan, but that excuse will not exempt you from this assignment. If the Japanese are not submissive and turn our envoys away, I rely on you to ensure their safe return. You are given this opportunity to demonstrate your loyalty, and I urge you to do your utmost.

The vice minister of war Ho-te and vice minister of ceremonies Yin-hung would be traveling to Japan as envoys of the Mongol Empire, and Koryŏ would be responsible for their safety and the mission's success. King Wŏnjong was given a copy of the Mongol state paper which was to be delivered to the Japanese:

> The emperor addresses this missive to the king of Japan. Rulers of small states sharing common boundaries have, since time immemo-

28

rial, endeavored to maintain a relationship of mutual trust and amity with one another. My forebears received the mandate of Heaven to bring China into the fold of our empire, and this we have done. Countless rulers of strange and distant lands have come to fear our might and to ask for our benevolent protection. Because the innocent people of Koryŏ were suffering from a long, disastrous war, when I ascended to the throne I withdrew our army, restored her lands, and allowed her people to return to their homes. Out of gratitude the king of Koryŏ presented himself at my court. Although in principle my relationship with the king of Koryŏ is that of sovereign and subject, in practice we enjoy the relationship of father and son. You and your people surely know this.

Koryŏ is easternmost among my tributary states. Japan, a close neighbor of Koryŏ, has sent envoys to China since earliest times. Since my accession, however, you have not once sent an envoy to establish amity with us. You apparently have not been informed of my wish. I am therefore sending an embassy for the express purpose of delivering this state paper so that you may be duly informed. It is my hope that henceforth we shall exchange appropriate formalities and that your people and mine will abide in peace and friendship. The sages have taught us that the universe consists of but one family; your refusal to enter into a relationship of amity with us would be a violation of the teaching of the sages. It would lead to an appeal to arms, a consequence neither you nor I would welcome. I urge Your Highness to reply as would befit propriety.

Edicts from Mongol emperors were ordinarily delivered in tubular metal containers five feet long and one foot in diameter. The large container itself was intimidating, but never before had it appeared so sinister, as if it possessed a dreadful will of its own.

King Wŏnjong summoned his princes and courtiers to the palace. The silence that prevailed in the great hall after the king had spoken indicated acquiescence: Kubilai had given his mandate, Koryŏ must comply.

Yi Chang-yong, the chief minister of state, saw dark storm clouds on the distant horizon expanding from within and threatening, like a curse, to spread across the heavens, covering the entire land. That the Mongols had addressed a state letter to Japan seeking amity meant that they now coveted Japan. They would accept nothing less than a pledge of fealty and the fullest ritual expression of tributary status. The Mongols would surely pursue this end regardless of the means required. And their intent, as stated in their letter, was clear: ". . . a refusal . . . would lead to an appeal to arms, a consequence neither you nor I would welcome."

Yi pondered how the Japanese might respond and how their response would affect Koryŏ. Whether or not the Japanese knew of the power of the Mongols seemed to matter little. Japan was protected by the sea; its people were by nature violent and warlike. It would not submit meekly to a summons however mighty the foreign nation that beckoned. The Japanese would probably turn the envoys away; in any case they would not honor the Mongols with a formal reply. Koryŏ would become the key to the Mongol plan to coerce Japan into accepting tributary status. The great Mongol army would be sent into the peninsula, its intimidating presence to be felt across the strait. Koryŏ's status would revert to that of the era of the late King Kojong. *Darughachi* would return to control its cities, exacting food for garrisoned troops and herding able-bodied Koreans into labor corps. Should the Mongols despatch an expeditionary force to Japan, Koryŏ would be subjected to even greater harshness than it had suffered during King Kojong's reign. Its soldiers would be sent off to fight a war on foreign soil, and its farmers would be conscripted to join the expedition as laborers.

No one spoke. Yi Chang-yong, his eyes closed, remained visibly downcast. The stifling silence was at last broken by Kim Chun, lord of Haeyang, who wielded great power as marshal of the nation's army.

"For Koryŏ's sake," the marshal said gravely, "we must pray that Japan will not offend Kubilai. Our own emissaries have a vital task to perform. They must convince the Japanese authorities of the enormity of Mongol might, then work toward bringing about a harmonious settlement. Should the day come when Mongol war vessels set sail for Japan, Koryŏ would be plunged into a despair from which it might never recover."

The truth the marshal spoke was chilling. Koryŏ's very survival depended on Japan's docile acceptance of the Mongol demand.

Koryŏ's emissaries were selected; they were the assistant privy councilor Song Kunbi and the censor Kim Ch'an. They would leave Kangdo with the Mongol embassy three days hence, on the twenty-eighth, fearful that any delay might anger Kubilai, who had said, "Do not use 'the fury of the wind and waves' as a pretext for shunning this duty." This statement was interpreted as a demand for prompt compliance.

Having made these decisions, the courtiers vented their resentment of that Korean Cho I, who, they thought, must have urged Kubilai to send an embassy to Japan. Denunciation of treachery on the part of their countrymen had become commonplace recently. Many Koreans had become Mongol subjects over the years, and the few who had risen high in Mongol officialdom had played insidious roles in every Mongol attempt to subjugate Koryŏ.

The most notorious among those expatriates was Hong Pogwŏn, who had devoted the last three decades of his life to helping the Mongols flay his homeland. Conspiring with his father, Hong Taesun, then a general in command of Inju, a province that stretched broadly southward from the banks of the Yalu River, Hong Pogwŏn surrendered to Sartaq during the first Mongol invasion of Koryŏ in 1231. Thereafter, his army of northern Koreans spearheaded every Mongol assault on his homeland. In recognition of his loyal endeavors, he was appointed senior military and civil administrator of expatriate Koreans and given the task of converting Koreans into loyal Mongol subjects. His army subsequently took uncounted walled cities in Koryŏ. However, in 1258, the year King Kojong first contemplated submitting to the Mongols, Hong Pogwŏn was executed for treason. The man who rose to power in his stead was his slanderer, the lord of Yŏngnyŏng Prince Chun, whom Koryŏ had sent to the Mongols in 1241 as a hostage representing the Koryŏ royal house. Having lived among the Mongols for more than two decades and now having replaced Hong Pogwŏn as the administrator of expatriate Koreans, Chun would soon have the power to do great injury to his motherland.

Little was known about Cho I. He was said to be a native of Hanam in South Kyŏngsang province, not far from the ports of Kimju (Kimhae) and Happ'o (Masanp'o) at the southern tip of the peninsula.

If Cho I had grown up in Hanam, he would have known about the Japanese traders who frequented the nearby port towns. He might have encouraged Kubilai to send an embassy to Japan, as the edict seemed to suggest, or perhaps he had been summoned by the Mongol authorities to tell them what he knew about Japan—nothing more. In any case, he must have played a role in the formulation of Kubilai's plan.

After leaving the palace, Yi Chang-yong walked through sleet toward his residence. The chief minister, now sixty-six, had become testy in his old age. Both a palanquin and a horse had been held in readiness for him at the main gate of the Inner City, but he had insisted on walking.

Despite its grand designation as a national capital, Kangdo was quite small. The Middle City, fortified by an encircling wall less than four miles in circumference, contained the royal palace, government offices, dwellings of royalty and courtiers, monasteries, quarters for the military, and merchants' shops. The royal palace, which overspread the northern quarter of the Middle City, was ringed by a protective wall; the enclosed palace grounds were called the Inner City. The palace and the government offices were located on level land; the other structures were situated on the slopes and skirts of three hills. One-third of the wall circumscribing the Middle City rose above the ridges of sheer cliffs along the southern boundary; visible from all parts of the city, that section inspired visions of an impenetrable wall of steel. The greater area of the city of Kangdo, some thirty-six miles in circumference, was called the Outer City. Kangdo thus consisted of the walled Inner City containing the royal palace, which lay within the protective walls of the Middle City or capital proper, which in turn lay within the defensive perimeter of the Outer City.

Kanghwa Island's topography and fortifications had at one time made it impregnable. But seven years earlier every section of the walls that had any tactical importance had been demolished.

Three vassals accompanied Yi Chang-yong as he trudged along the mired road leading to his residence more than half a mile away. Strollers noticed Yi's unsteady gait and stepped aside to yield the road to the dour old man some recognized as the chief minister.

Yi occasionally stepped into deep mire but seemed oblivious of the difficulty. Absorbed in thought, he was trying to devise a way to keep the Mongol envoys from going to Japan. Marshal Kim Chun had said, "We must pray that Japan will not offend Kubilai," but prayers offered no assurance. The Koreans must prevent the embassy from reaching Japan. But how? Yi knew that he must himself convince the Mongols that a voyage to Japan was folly. He vacillated —should he meet with them or send an appeal in writing? Although he scarcely expected the Mongols to defy Kubilai by yielding to a Korean's plea, he resolved to try. Surely the envoys did not relish their mission, for the voyage was hazardous. Even if they reached Japan, their fate was uncertain. If the Japanese proved to be humble, well and good. If they were not, the envoys would be accused of dereliction, even though they had fulfilled their assignment. Theirs was an unenviable mission. Yi was reasonably certain that they would not dismiss his plea outright—he would exploit their fear. And if his attempt became known, only he would be punished.

By the time Yi entered the gate of his residence, he had made up his mind to counsel the Mongols in writing. They could decide among themselves whether to accept the import of his letter; only they would know if they did. If they altered their plans, only they would know whether he had influenced them.

In the quiet of his room, Yi composed this letter addressed to Ho-te, the Mongol ambassador to Japan:

Japan lies a thousand leagues across the sea. It has had traffic with China since time immemorial, but it never, in any year, came forth with tributary offerings. China therefore did not bother with Japan. When Japan sent envoys to China, they were received graciously. When envoys ceased to come, Japan was quickly forgotten, for China did not profit from the relationship nor was its dignity affected by the termination of the relationship. His Imperial Majesty today reigns from on high, and every nation that basks in the light of the sun and moon has become his subject. To China small barbarian nations are of no more significance than insects, and which among them would dare not submit? Yet we must remember that the category of insects includes the hornet and the scorpion, both with poisonous stings.

It would be the height of imprudence to dignify Japan with state papers. Japan's arrogance is such that its king dared to present Emperor Wen-ti of the Sui Dynasty [A.D. 590–617] with a paper stating: "The Son of Heaven of the nation where the sun rises addresses this missive to the Son of Heaven of the nation in which the sun sets." No one knows whether Japan continues to maintain such airs. If the Mongol state paper is delivered to Japan and if Japan returns an impudent reply, your great nation could not ignore that reply without suffering a loss of mien. A consequent attempt to seize Japan would expose your soldiers to the hazards of crossing stormy seas and occupying an unsafe land. I believe that your great nation has never wished to extend its benevolent rule over Japan, but is now tempted to do so simply because someone chanced to recommend it. Though such an insignificant country may be favored with an imperial pronouncement, that gracious act would yield no benefits. Is it possible that Japan has not heard of the might and benevolence of your great nation? If it has, its failure to send envoys is due entirely to its reliance on the safety provided by its insularity. As the sages, in their infinite wisdom would have urged, observe Japan with patience: if the Japanese send envoys to you, enjoin them to bring their country within your fold; if they do not, ignore them and let them continue to abide in their small, forgotten world.

Although I wish to be received in audience by His Imperial Majesty again, to bask in his graciousness, I languish in a remote land, all the while wishing to serve him loyally, myriadfold.

Yi's letter was given that night to the keeper of the royal records Pan Pu, who had been assigned to Ho-te as official host. Pan Pu was instructed to place the letter in Ho-te's hands.

His self-imposed task completed, Yi Chang-yong throbbed with fatigue. But he knew he had done what he could to stave off a crisis, the second since the surrender to the Mongols. In the first, two years earlier, King Wŏnjong had been summoned to Yen-tu. The courtiers, who had felt complacently secure in Koryŏ's new status as a Mongol protectorate, were shaken. Suddenly dismayed, they feared that Kubilai meant to degrade Koryŏ further. They vehemently objected to the king's going, questioning whether he would return once he left Korean soil. Yi Chang-yang alone urged submission to Kubilai's bidding. He did not deny the risk. Nevertheless, he asserted, it was a Heaven-sent opportunity for Koryŏ to ingratiate itself with the Mongols. "Should there be any mishap, let my clan be executed with me!" he had declared to the court. There was no mishap, and the king had returned. Yet the new crisis held possibilities far more dreadful.

Yi Chang-yong accompanied the embassy to the Ch'ojijin ferry point at the southern tip of Kanghwa Island. The Mongol envoys, Ho-te and Yin-hung, and their Korean assistants, Song Kunbi and Kim Ch'an, would cross the channel and travel overland to Happ'o, whence they would embark for Japan. More than one hundred people had come to the ferry to wish them well. Yi easily recognized Ho-te, a man of commanding stature. They exchanged nods but did not speak to each each other. Yi wondered if his letter had made any impression on the Mongol. He did not know Ho-te, and he felt troubled as he watched the ship leave the dock. He regretted not having written more forcefully about the arrogance of the Japanese and the perils of crossing the stormy sea.

In the "Biography of Yi Chang-yong" in the *History of Koryŏ,* Yi is thus described:

> Yi Chang-yong, known as Ingi in his childhood and subsequently by his style, Hyŏnbo, is a descendant six generations removed of the chief councilor Yi Chayŏn. Chang-yong entered officialdom during the reign of King Kojong and, in 1260, the first year of King Wŏnjong's reign, was appointed assistant privy councilor and concurrently as grand marshal, director for the compilation of the nation's history, and supervisor of the Office of the Census. In 1264 he accompanied King Wŏnjong to the Mongol court. . . . On that occasion he was feted by Wang Oh, scholar of the Hanlin Academy. As the singer Wu Yen-kao sang the songs "Man and Moon in Harmony" and "Spring is Heaven-sent," Chang-yong sang the words softly in precise tune with him. Oh came up to Chang-yong, grasped his hand, and spoke these words of praise: "You know this song well even though you do not know Chinese. How well versed you are in music!" And his respect for Chang-yong grew immeasurably. The Mongol emperor, having heard Chang-yong speak, called him "Chief Minister Yi, he of skillful speech."

In December, the men at the royal court in Kangdo were informed of the Mongol embassy's abrupt return to Koryŏ, and they gloomily pondered the consequence of failure of a mission in which they had been assigned a specific role. What excuse besides shipwreck would Kubilai condone? He would be enraged if he were told that fear of the stormy sea had caused the embassy to turn back. A hopeful few reminded the others that the Korean emissaries were essentially diplomatic guides, fully subservient to the Mongol envoys; therefore Koryŏ could not be blamed. Whatever the reasons, others contended, Koryŏ had been ordered to conduct the Mongol envoys to the court of Japan and would be charged with failure to discharge that responsibility. During these deliberations King Wŏnjong often recalled the chilling passage in Kubilai's edict: " 'The fury of the wind and waves' is a well-worn phrase; do not make it a pretext for shunning this duty." Because Kubilai had been explicit on this point, he doubted that his nation would be forgiven.

The travelers were back in Kangdo in January, and what they told the leaders of the Koryŏ government was disheartening. The embassy had gone as far as the coastal island of Kŏje, where they saw a sea made turbulent by winds that sent waves soaring high into the heavens. Aware of the perils of crossing the Korea Strait to reach the Japanese island of Tsushima, the Mongol and Korean envoys consulted one another and decided to turn back. The Koryŏ court could not very well chastise the Mongols. Its anger over the mission's failure was directed at its own representatives, Song Kunbi and Kim Ch'an.

"Did you expect us to order the Mongol envoys to take to the sea against their wishes?" Song Kunbi protested. He begged the king's permission to go to the Mongol court so that he might fully describe the series of events to Emperor Kubilai.

Chief Minister Yi Chang-yong had remained silent, but he was now compelled to make a disclosure: he had written the Mongol envoys the day before they left Kangdo; his letter must have influenced their decision to turn back.

"Emperor Kubilai's anger over the embassy's failure to reach Japan will be severe," Yi explained, "but not so dreadful as the fury that would have been aroused had his subjects reached Japanese shores. Let us maintain that turbulence prevented them from sailing. It is the only excuse that might exonerate the members of the mission. Song Kunbi must not be allowed to disclose anything that might place the Mongol envoys in jeopardy, for the kingdom of Koryŏ is deeply indebted to them."

This unexpected revelation bewildered the courtiers, impressing them into silence.

"But wouldn't the Mongol envoys disclose everything regardless?" Kim Ch'an asked apprehensively.

"They might," Yi replied, "and we must prepare for that eventuality through my condemnation. Kubilai might be assuaged, and Koryŏ exonerated, if we were to report that the instigator, Yi Chang-yong, has already been punished. I anticipated such a consequence when I wrote my letter."

As a precaution, the Koryŏ government decided to banish Yi Chang-yong to the island of Yŏnghŭng, and Pan Pu to Ch'aeun Island for the crime of delivering Yi's letter to the Mongols. The Mongol envoys learned about this turn of events when government officers came to their lodging to apprehend Pan Pu. Ho-te hastened to the royal palace, bringing Yi's letter with him.

"I shall take this letter back with me and enter a plea on Yi's behalf," Ho-te said to King Wŏnjong. "I hope that His Imperial Majesty will pardon Yi. The government of Koryŏ need not punish Yi, for he merely gave me his opinion. The private opinion of one Yi Chang-yong did not influence my decision. I turned back because tempests prevented us from sailing." Yi and Pan were thus absolved, thanks to Ho-te's intercession.

When Ho-te and Yin-hung left Kangdo later that month, Song Kunbi went with them. This memorial, which Song was to present to Kubilai, was composed on the king's behalf by Yi Chang-yong:

In compliance with Your Majesty's instructions, I despatched my subject Song Kunbi to conduct your embassy to Japan. The party sailed to Kŏje Island, from which Tsushima Island could be glimpsed in the distance. Seeing the raging wind send waves soaring high into the heavens across an expanse of a myriad *li,* Song did not dare subject your emissaries to the risk of proceeding further. Had they reached Tsushima, they would have encountered people who are obdurate and unruly and have no sense of propriety. What could your envoys have done if those inhabitants had become violent? Song, therefore,

conducted the embassy back to the mainland. Koryŏ has not established diplomatic relations with Japan; men from Tsushima sometimes come to Kimju, but only to trade. Since Your Majesty's accession to the throne, we have become deeply indebted to you for your
compassion. That my country has found respite from thirty years of
war is due to your benevolence, which is as boundless as the sky. I
have made a vow, therefore, to repay this debt of gratitude. May
Heaven be witness to my pledge to do all in my power on Your Majesty's behalf.

Ho-te and Yin-hung returned in August, with the following pronouncement:

Earlier, when I despatched an embassy to invite the Japanese to my
court, I entrusted you with the responsibility of conducting it to
Japan. You dared to let the embassy return, its mission unfulfilled.
You fear that the Japanese may advise me of the true state of affairs in
your country if they establish diplomatic relations with us. You therefore conspired to foredoom the mission to failure. Many of your
countrymen live in our capital, and your contrivance was easily discerned. Heaven is difficult to deceive; humanity treasures sincerity.
You must reflect well on the many times you have failed to honor
your word. I now entrust you with the matter pertaining to Japan.
You are to convey my message to the Japanese and to admonish
them, persisting in your efforts until you succeed. You have stated,
"Your benevolence is as boundless as the sky. I have made a vow,
therefore, to repay this debt of gratitude." Would not fulfillment of
this task be a way to fulfill that vow?

The pronouncement was unambiguous in its condemnation of
King Wŏnjong's artful memorial; and it assigned Koryŏ the entire
responsibility for establishing amity between Japan and the Mongol
Empire.

A conference of ministers was held immediately. In view of the
severity of Kubilai's message, Koryŏ would have to send an embassy
to Japan. After much deliberation, the keeper of the royal records
Pan Pu was appointed emissary at Yi Chang-yong's recommenda-
tion. Pan Pu was probably best qualified to carry out this difficult
mission. He was familiar with the recent events; he was known to be

a man of sound judgment, adept at accommodating the unexpected; he would not err in judging crucial matters at critical times.

Approximately a month later, on the twenty-third of September,
Pan Pu set sail from Kanghwa Island on a direct voyage to Japan. Yi
Chang-yong gave him no special instructions, and at parting only
said, "I shall pray for your safe return. And I shall pray that you succeed, for the outcome of this mission will determine the fate of our
country."

Pan Pu was entrusted with a Koryŏ state paper for Japan, to be
delivered together with the state paper the Mongol emperor had
earlier addressed to Japan's king. The Mongol paper was dated
August of the third year of the Chih-yuan era, or 1266. The Koryŏ
paper, dated September of 1267, was composed by Yi Chang-yong.
The fair copy, bearing the Koryŏ national seal, was the result of
many painstaking drafts:

> My country has been subordinate to the great Mongol nation and has
> abided by its policies for many years. The Mongol emperor, benevo-
> lent and enlightened, regards the entire world as one family and favors
> distant nations equally with his own. His virtues are admired by all
> people who bask in the light of the sun and the moon. He now
> wishes to establish amity with your country and has stated to me in
> his rescript: "Japan lies in close proximity to your country, and its
> institutions and government are praiseworthy. It has sent envoys to
> China since the eras of the Han and T'ang dynasties. I therefore took
> special pains to despatch an embassy to Japan, but you cited 'the fury
> of the wind and waves' as your excuse for failing to conduct the
> embassy safely to Japan." The purport of his message is stern and inci-
> sive. I am therefore obliged to despatch my own emissary to deliver
> the Mongol emperor's paper to you. You have enjoyed amity with
> China in eras past. The Mongol emperor wishes to restore amity with
> your country not for the purpose of acquiring tributary offerings, but
> to have China known throughout the world as one nation comprising
> all nations. Should he receive a delegation from your country, he will
> welcome it cordially. You will know the truth of my words once you
> have established amity with the Mongol Empire. My emissary will
> soon touch on Japanese soil. I appeal to you to heed his urging.

Toward the end of that year, King Wŏnjong sent his younger
brother, the lord of An'gyŏng Prince Ch'ang, to deliver his New

Year's congratulations to the Mongol court. The chilling report which Prince Ch'ang brought back in February appalled the men at Kangdo. He said he had informed Kubilai that Koryŏ had despatched Pan Pu to Japan as the emperor had commanded it. Instead of acknowledging Koryŏ's compliance, Kubilai erupted in fury, condemning Koryŏ's failure to fulfill the obligations of a protectorate. Specifying the delay in moving the capital, the hopelessly inferior quality of tributary offerings, and Koryŏ's denial of presumed diplomatic intercourse with Japan, he angrily denounced Koryŏ's perfidy.

Shortly following Prince Ch'ang's return, an emissary arrived in Kangdo bearing Kubilai's rescript, which expressed in writing the great wrath which Ch'ang had described orally. It concluded: "I have taken the extraordinary measure of despatching my personal emissary to deliver this rescript. You are to make a complete and truthful disclosure in a letter, to be delivered to me by the lord of Haeyang Kim Chun and your royal advisor Yi Chang-yong. All my charges are to be answered."

Having met and discussed Kubilai's demand that day, the Koryŏ court decided to send Yi but to exempt Kim Chun, preoccupied as he was with planning the relocation of the capital. Kim Chun, to speak the truth, was disgusted with his fellow courtiers, who shifted back and forth between elation and consternation with every new pronouncement from Kubilai. And he did not want to be a member of a mission that promised no assurance of its emissaries returning alive.

This was to be the third and perhaps the last time that Yi Chang-yong, then sixty-eight, would place his life in jeopardy for his country. Before he left, he sought an audience with King Wŏnjong to impart his counsel: His Royal Highness must return to the former capital as quickly as possible so that the spirits of the land might find repose.

The project of moving the court was a nagging burden. In the nine years since the Koryŏ monarchy had agreed to comply with Kubilai's wish, little progress had been made in the task of rebuilding Kaegyŏng. Bereft of funds, the government could no longer employ carpenters or laborers. Construction had come to a halt two years earlier. To make matters worse, during the great rains of the previous year all the lumber stored at the upper reaches of the Han and Naktong rivers had been washed away along with the topsoil of the river basins. Moreover, a sizable faction at court led by Marshal Kim Chun was advocating an indefinite postponement because of a military reality: the strength of Koryŏ's small army, however formidable on Kanghwa Island, would be reduced a hundredfold if the units were moved to Kaegyŏng. But others were concerned that failure to honor the promise would give the Mongols another excuse to exact cruel demands.

"Though we may not be able to rebuild the city of Kaegyŏng, let us at least rebuild the palace," Yi urged King Wŏnjong. "You may sojourn there in the summer, but return to Kangdo in the winter. You can say that you are emulating the Mongol example of maintaining capitals in both Karakorum and Yen-tu."

King Wŏnjong thereupon promised Yi that he would establish the office of Overseer of the Alternation of Capitals.

Yi Chang-yong left Kangdo in April of 1268 with a retinue of two dozen men. Five years had gone by since his previous visit to the Mongol court, and the added years of age weighed heavily on him as he spent the same long hours on horseback. After traveling through Sŏgyŏng and arriving at the banks of the Taedong River, Yi gazed fondly at the broad leisurely flow which, he thought, he might not see again. He contemplated the careworn faces of the women laundering in the shallows. The conspicuous presence of women and children in the vicinity of Sŏgyŏng and other cities attested to the reduction of the male population during the thirty years of Mongol depredation.

As they traveled through Ŭiju, they learned that some of the inhabitants, recalling the relative prosperity during the Mongol occupation, yearned for a return to that era. Whenever Yi heard that sentiment expressed, he sank into the deepest gloom.

Yi Chang-yong arrived in Yen-tu in the middle of May. He proceeded directly to the splendid palace at the center of the city to seek an audience with Emperor Kubilai. He was told to be seated on a stone dais at the palace entrance, and was kept waiting there for several hours while Kubilai received emissaries from other foreign states. As he waited, his blemished face was burned dark by the merciless rays of the sun.

The instant Yi came into his presence, Kubilai began to shout. Not knowing the Mongol language, Yi could only listen fearfully to what he presumed to be a tirade. Soon he heard an interpreter whose calm, measured Korean contrasted oddly with Kubilai's unintelligible ranting.

"I ordered your country to stand ready to provide me with troops to assist in war. You have not informed me of the precise numerical strength of your army. Indeed, you have been deceitful. I was informed by Prince Chun, a hostage from your country, that Koryŏ has a standing army of forty thousand soldiers and ten thousand laborers. I therefore sent you an edict in which I stated that since your country indeed possesses a sizable army, you are to retain ten thousand for the defense of your own country and despatch the other forty thousand to assist me in battle. You replied that your country does not possess an army of fifty thousand, that Chun does not speak the truth, that your assertions may be verified if I should send my emissary with the informant to inspect your army. I need not have summoned you if Koryŏ had provided me with an accurate count of its troops."

Yi Chang-yong lifted his gaze. The interpreter, much to his surprise, was a Korean—a man with sallow complexion, in his midtwenties. Although he had well-formed features, his cold, still eyes told Yi that he felt no emotions. Not even the eyes of a disinterested foreigner could be so indifferent. He gave no indication of recognizing Yi as a fellow countryman.

Again Yi heard Kubilai's thunderous shouts. Following on the young man's unimpassioned, low-pitched monotone, Kubilai's hoarse shouting now had a curiously hollow ring. An unexpected lull of silence caused Yi to look up again. He noticed a middle-aged man of aristocratic bearing entering the room and recognized him as the lord of Yŏngnyŏng Prince Chun, whom Koryŏ had sent to the Mongols many years earlier as a child hostage. Chun had spent his life among the Mongols, and was now inclined to cast his own country in an unfavorable light. Apparently summoned to participate in this audience, he bowed to the emperor and quietly seated himself. His innate nobility was manifest in his gentle features and dignified carriage.

Kubilai resumed his shouting, his face now flushed. He would work himself into a feverish pitch and then pause, breathing hard. Any lull in Kubilai's ranting was a signal for the young Korean to interpret, invariably in a calm monotone. Having finished, the interpreter would strike an attitude of eager concentration, perking his unusually large ears. Yi would try to seize that opportunity to speak. But Kubilai's would begin to rant, cutting him off.

"Return to your country and prepare an accurate report of your military strength," said Kubilai ultimately. "I am about to send my armies to conquer the Sung Empire, then Japan. I regard your country as a member of my family. If Koryŏ were placed in peril, would I not come to your rescue? My reply to arrogance is conquest. Koryŏ is duty-bound to supply troops to assist me in war. Return to your country and tell your king to provide me with a thousand warships, each with a capacity of three to four thousand piculs of rice."

"We obey your every command," Yi replied, with a calmness that belied his dismay. "Though we may have the material to construct the ships, I regret our inability to mobilize shipwrights in sufficient numbers to build so many ships."

"Do not defy me!" Kubilai responded. "We need not go back to antiquity to find examples of ways in which treachery is rewarded. Not many years ago, during the era of Jenghis Khan, the king of Ho-hsi presented a woman to the court as he sought peace. At that time he said, 'Should Your Majesty ride to conquer the Jurchens, I shall serve as your right hand. Should you ride to conquer the Muslims, I shall serve as your left hand.' When the great khan was ready to ride against the Muslims, he ordered the king of Ho-hsi to aid him, but the latter refused. The great khan attacked him again and again and destroyed him. If you did not know this, know it now. Build a thousand vessels. Mobilize your troops and send them to me."

"My country once had an army of forty thousand troops," Yi

replied, "but most them died during the thirty years of warfare. Though people may speak of a hundred, a thousand detachments, those detachments exist in name alone."

"Of course men have died. But your country has not been without women. Do you dare tell me there have been no newborn?"

"Thanks to your great benevolence, we have not had war these past nine years. Our boys have grown, but they are not yet old enough to become soldiers."

Chun stepped forth and was about to speak, but hesitated as Yi directed a sharp glance at him. "I do not wish to bicker with a countryman in Your Majesty's presence," Yi said. "If you have doubts about the size of Koryŏ's army, I ask that you send us a responsible man to take an accurate count of our troops."

"I have nothing more to say, but I shall soon test your words," Kubilai said, and rose. Yi Chang-yong stood and bowed deeply, maintaining that pose until Kubilai and his Korean retainers had left the room. Yi later learned that the young interpreter was Hong Tagu, son of the late Hong Pogwŏn and grandson of Hong Taesun, who had turned maliciously against his native Koryŏ. Yi had heard of Hong Tagu. A favorite of Emperor Kubilai along with Prince Chun, this young Korean was now the senior military and civil administrator of expatriate Koreans, and was said to wield even greater influence than Chun. Hong Tagu was becoming a name to be reckoned with in his home country.

Yi dwelt in gloom during his party's homeward journey, but he endured well the harshness of travel. Two of their horses collapsed, victims of the oppressive heat, and one of Yi's retainers was felled by sickness. Yet Yi pressed on, anxious to be back on native soil. The Yalu River was then swollen by floods, and the travelers were detained for five days at a village on the northern bank.

*

Yi Chang-yong returned to Kangdo at the end of June and presented King Wŏnjong with this report: "Kubilai has commanded that our nation build one thousand warships, and that we submit a report specifying the number of men in our nation's army. If we provide Kubilai with an accurate count, I fear he will appropriate that number of troops for his own use."

Although the king paled when he heard this, he was inclined to think that these harsh commands were Kubilai's means of conveying displeasure. Once, when Kubilai had berated him for Koryŏ's failure to fulfill the obligations of a tributary state, Wŏnjong wrote him describing Koryŏ's state of debilitation. He remembered well the sympathy with which Kubilai had responded. This time again, he thought, Koryŏ would be exonerated if he provided Kubilai with a vivid description of his country's plight. At the court of Koryŏ, King Wŏnjong was consistently alone in defending Kubilai's actions. When he was crown prince, he had met with Kubilai at a small village outside K'ai-feng, and again at Yen-ching. When he was summoned to the Mongol court in the fifth year of his reign, he was received in audience by Kubilai at the imperial palace and again at the detached palace on Mount Wan-shou. What he remembered best was Kubilai's imperious yet benign expression, his captivating manner of speech, and that indefinable warmth in which he had felt himself enfolded during those interviews. Wŏnjong cherished those memories.

Yi Chang-yong could guess his king's thoughts. "As a tiger approaches a rabbit, its eyes are said to be incredibly gentle," he said to the king. "Then it emits a roar that shakes the mountains and gorges, paralyzing the rabbit. Kubilai's demand for warships is but a prelude to that roar. How else may we interpret it?"

King Wŏnjong continued to believe that Koryŏ would be forgiven when Pan Pu returned from his mission to Japan. Kubilai was displeased because of Koryŏ's failure to conduct the Mongol embassy to Japan. If Pan Pu fulfilled the mission originally entrusted to the Mongol embassy, the dark billowing clouds about to engulf Koryŏ would surely disperse.

Pan Pu returned to Kangdo in early July, more than ten months after his departure. His report, in brief, stated that he left Kangdo in September, found fair winds at Happ'o in late October, and crossed over to Tsushima Island. Detained for more than a month by tempestuous weather, he set sail for Japan but was forced back to Tsushima by a turbulent sea. A second sailing also failed. His third attempt in late January took him to Dazaifu, the westernmost head-quarters of the Japanese shogun's government. He was kept there for five months, denied permission to proceed to the capital. The recipient of few courtesies, he was given no reply to the message he had conveyed to the Japanese. Although he presented them with Koryŏ's gifts and alternately pleaded and remonstrated with them, they paid him no heed. He ultimately handed the Mongol and Koryŏ state papers over to the Japanese, but they did not honor him with a written reply.

Pan Pu met only with King Wŏnjong and Yi Chang-yong, then left Kangdo the following day to report to Kubilai in Yen-tu. It was a time when all of officialdom was becoming preoccupied with the attempt to fulfill Kubilai's demands. Crown Prince Sim had the task of supervising the shipbuilding, and Kim Chun was in charge of military conscription. Never before had so many vessels been seen plying the strait between Kanghwa Island and the Korean mainland.

At the beginning of August, Koryŏ despatched an emissary bearing this message to the Mongols: "Mobilization in all the provinces has brought together an army of only ten thousand men; officials in the coastal regions have begun constructing the one thousand vessels."

*

In mid-October, Wang Kuo-ch'ang, Liu Chieh, and twelve others were sent by the Mongols to evaluate Koryŏ's armed strength and capacity to build warships. Residing at Kangdo, Wang oversaw the mobilization of troops and Liu reviewed information on the construction of ships; they would conclude their evaluation at year's end. Knowing well that the Koryŏ government would not be allowed even one mistake, the crown prince and Kim Chun dared not slacken their efforts to inspect the many sites for shipbuilding and conscription throughout the peninsula. Seldom were they in Kangdo.

Wang and Liu soon left Kangdo with Korean guides to look at Hŭksan Island. A small island among the many off the west coast of South Chŏlla province, Hŭksan had a bay large enough to harbor hundreds of ships. Clearly the Mongol officials had gone to Hŭksan to study its suitability as a staging area for the invasion of Japan.

Although Koryŏ seemed to have come under the eye of a storm moving southward from the land of the Mongols, King Wŏnjong remained optimistic. He expected Pan Pu to bring back encouraging news from the Mongol court.

Pan Pu returned from Yen-tu in mid-November and, to the king's surprise, was accompanied by Ho-te and Yin-hung, who delivered this edict addressed to King Wŏnjong:

> When I earlier entrusted you with the task of conducting my embassy to Japan, you provided me with deceptive counsel. "Your emissaries must not," you wrote, "be needlessly imperiled by the tempestuous sea." How then was Pan Pu able to cross the sea to Japan? You said that Pan Pu reached Japan but was turned away by an inhospitable people. You are guilty of shameful and irreverent deceit, and are not to be trusted. I am despatching Ho-te and Yin-hung again as my envoys to Japan. They are to be conducted by your vassals, and I expect you to ensure their safe arrival in Japan. Do not dare to obstruct their passage as you did before.

After several conferences, the director of the chancellery Shin Sajŏn, Vice Minister Chin Chahu, and Pan Pu were chosen to serve as intermediaries for the Mongol envoys to Japan.

The Mongol embassy left Kangdo for Japan on the fourth of December. The party consisted of more than seventy men, including eight envoys from the Mongol nation and four from the kingdom of Koryŏ. The expense of despatching this large mission to Japan was to be borne by Koryŏ. King Wŏnjong and all of Koryŏ's officialdom were at the Ch'ojijin ferry point to bid the mission farewell. The party would, again, cross the channel, then travel overland to Happ'o port.

Wang Kuo-ch'ang and Liu Chieh had, in the meantime, returned from Hŭksan Island. On the day after the mission left, the crown prince accompanied Liu Chieh on a tour of inspection of the shipyards along the western coast. Kim Chun similarly accompanied Wang Kuo-ch'ang to Kaegyŏng and stood beside him as he inspected the ten thousand troops that stood in formation on the spacious grounds of the partly completed royal palace.

Their mission accomplished, Wang and Liu left for their Mongol homeland. An unsettling incident occurred in the wake of their departure: the lord of Haeyang Kim Chun was assassinated by his subordinate Im Yŏn, an assistant commissioner in the Bureau of Military Affairs. Kim Chun was a soldier who had risen from the ranks by virtue of meritorious service. Appointed royal advisor with a stipend of one thousand households and then awarded the title Lord of Haeyang, he became the supreme authority within the military and stood at equal political prominence with Yi Chang-yong. He resented the coercive stance of the Mongols and consistently refused to bow to their edicts. Inhospitable to their emissaries, he antagonized them with outrages that could have brought retaliation against the nation. He defied Kubilai's orders to report to the Mongol court together with Yi Chang-yong. Mounting criticism of Kim Chun gave Im Yŏn justification for eliminating the superior he had long detested. It snowed on the day of the assassination, and the snowfall continued through the remainder of the year. It snowed more heavily during those few weeks than at any time in recent memory.

*

The party of the Mongol embassy to Japan returned to Kangdo on the sixteenth of March of the following year, 1269. According to the envoys, the mission put to shore on Tsushima Island and presented the Japanese with the state papers. The officials on Tsushima would not accept them, nor would they allow the party to continue on to the main Japanese islands. The mission returned to Koryŏ, bringing with them two Japanese, Tōjirō and Yashirō.

King Wŏnjong ordered Shin Sajŏn to accompany the Mongol envoys back to their country and present the emperor with a report on Koryŏ's behalf. Shin Sajŏn returned to Kangdo in early June with tidings that caused the government of Koryŏ to rejoice. He reported that Kubilai had said to him: "Your king sent you to Japan in compliance with my orders. In spite of many perils, you went to an unknown land and returned safely, and you are to be commended." Kubilai said to the two Japanese captives: "You are the first to visit us in a long while. I want envoys from your country to come to pay us homage. I shall not burden them with unreasonable demands. I simply wish to have recorded for posterity the fact that your country accorded me the courtesy of sending envoys to my court." The Japanese were entertained regally, taken on an excursion to Kubilai's detached palace on Mount Wan-shou, then allowed to return to their country.

On the day Shin brought back those tidings, King Wŏnjong summoned the two men he held in closest confidence—his younger brother, the lord of An'gyŏng Prince Ch'ang, and his chief minister Yi Chang-yong—and related these thoughts to them. Building a thousand warships was the most pressing of Kubilai's demands, and the attempt to comply had brought havoc to the whole land. He, the king, could not understand why Kubilai would want to conquer Japan. Perhaps Kubilai would be satisfied if he could establish diplomatic relations with Japan. Ho-te touched at Tsushima Island but was not allowed to continue on to the main Japanese islands, and the Japanese authorities refused to accept his credentials. Kubilai apparently was not annoyed; indeed, he invited the two Japanese into his palace, awarded them gifts, and ordered their safe return home. Surely he did not intend to make war with Japan now. Although he had ordered Koryŏ to organize an auxiliary army of ten thousand men—a task already accomplished—he had not issued orders to that army. Was this not an indication of a fundamental change in his policy toward Japan?

"I am quite certain," the king said, "that soon we shall be told to stop building ships, and that the newly conscripted troops will be able to return to their farms."

"But Kubilai is now engaged in a decisive war against the Sung Empire," the lord of An'gyŏng replied. "He needs warships to assault the walled city of Huai-yang on the bank of the Han River in south China. They say he has ordered the provincial administrators of Shensi and Szechwan to build warships. The ships and troops of Koryŏ will probably be diverted to that campaign. I doubt he will rescind his orders. He might, of course, when he has finished off the Sung, whenever that might be."

"I beg to differ with Your Highnesses," Yi Chang-yong said. "I believe that Kubilai has merely postponed his campaign to conquer Japan, and will never rescind his orders. He might wish to utilize our ships and troops in his war against the Sung, as the lord of An'gyŏng has said. But would he commandeer ships over such a great distance? Would the troop strength of the Mongols would be at such a low ebb as to require the help of a small Korean army? The lord of An'gyŏng might be correct. Yet I cannot believe that Koryŏ will be freed from Mongol exactions when the campaign against the Sung is over. I do not believe that Kubilai needs more warships or troops. His purpose in forcing exactions on Koryŏ is to sap our nation's strength. He wants to reduce us to utter poverty and despair, and then to bring us into the fold of his empire.

"However weak or small the object of his conquest may be," Yi continued, "Kubilai will need a pretext for annexation. He will eventually conquer the Sung, and then he will shift his gaze to Japan. The Mongols could not take Kanghwa Island because it lies across a narrow channel. Would they dare send an expedition across the open sea without our help? If they should decide to conquer Japan, we would be the victims, for a gigantic army would march through Koryŏ to sail from the southern coast of this peninsula. The Mongols might decide against launching their fleet from Koryŏ. Even then, they will continue to burden us with one demand after another on the pretext of requiring Koryŏ's support. When I recall the suffering we endured for thirty years as our land was being trampled underfoot by Mongol horsemen, I know we shall be able to endure their exactions, however harsh they might be."

Yi said what he had known some day he must. His king believed that a sympathetic Kubilai would allow Koryŏ to heal; so too did the lord of An'gyŏng Prince Ch'ang, though his expectations were not as high as the king's. Yi did not. He had twice been in the land of the Mongols to be received in audience by Kubilai. Unlike King Wŏnjong, he had detected no warmth in Kubilai, whose eyes, complexion, and voice seemed to lack any quality one might describe as human. Kubilai struck him as a creature capable of devising outrages that would horrify a civilized mind.

CHAPTER 3

ONE DAY in mid-June, a visitor called at Yi Chang-yong's residence. It was Im Yŏn, the commander who had assassinated his superior officer, Marshal Kim Chun. As Yi led him to an inner room opening onto a garden, he heard the neighing of horses. The tumult outside the walls indicated the presence of a large military force.

Im Yŏn was excited, but he kept his eyes leveled at Yi's as he described his scheme to banish King Wŏnjong to a coastal island and invest his younger brother, the lord of An'gyŏng Prince Ch'ang, with regal authority. "The most agonizing deliberation led me to this decision. You might not agree with me, but you cannot change my mind. My reasons for wanting to dictate a royal succession are evident. Koryŏ's present crisis cannot be resolved by King Wŏnjong, a puppet in the hands of the Mongol emperor he so admires, nor by the inept crown prince. Unless changes are brought about now, Koryŏ will soon be annexed by the Mongol Empire. When the lord of An'gyŏng Prince Ch'ang is king, I will be able to reverse the court's policies and imbue the people with a new pride that will inspire them to fight for their country."

Yi Chang-yong told Im Yŏn that his plan was sensible enough. Im had given a fairly honest statement of his reasons, but Yi knew that he had left some things unsaid. Although Im had served the royal court well by eliminating Kim Chun, the king could not trust this blundering middle-aged soldier who was inclined to impetuous, violent action. Knowing that he could not gain the king's trust, Im Yŏn had decided to use his present authority to banish Wŏnjong and enthrone Prince Ch'ang, whom he could easily manipulate. Yi assumed that the royal palace was surrounded by Im's troops. Recognizing the futility of objection, he suggested a sensible alternative:

rather than banish King Wŏnjong to a coastal island, Im should confine him in the detached palace. If Im dared to exile his king, not only would he be branded a rebel, he would also incur Kubilai's wrath; he would be well advised to attribute the king's abdication to impaired health. Im Yŏn gratefully accepted Yi's counsel. And Yi was grateful that he did, for he could now protect the king from harm while working to stave off intervention by the Mongols.

The royal succession took place the following day. Under Im Yŏn's watchful eyes, Prince Ch'ang ascended to the throne and Wŏnjong was removed to the detached palace. Crown Prince Sim had left more than two months earlier to pay homage to the Mongols, and his absence suited Im Yŏn's purpose.

Three days later, Yi sought out Kim Pang-gyŏng, the assistant commissioner of the Bureau of Military Affairs, and the two visited King Wŏnjong secretly. They begged the king to be patient while they worked toward restoring his sovereignty. So long as he and Kim Pang-gyŏng remained in their respective posts, Yi assured the king, they would be able to steer Koryŏ clear of disaster. Kim Pang-gyŏng, by nature laconic, straightened his tall, cranelike body and mumbled softly. Neither Yi nor the king heard him distinctly. He seemed to have said: "Although Im Yŏn can easily be chastised, such action might well invite Mongol intercession. Please exercise forbearance . . . a while longer. Please, a while longer!" The mere fact that Kim Pang-gyŏng had spoken words of counsel inspired confidence. Kim, whom Yi considered the most trustworthy among the military, was fifty-eight years old, Yi's junior by eleven years.

Kim Pang-gyŏng, whose style-name was Ponyŏn, was from Andong. He was said to be descended directly from King Kyŏngsun of the kingdom of Silla. His father, Hyŏjuk, known as an upright man, had been appointed to a post in the secretariat of the Ministry of War upon passing the government examinations, and eventually was admitted to the Hanlin Academy, where membership was restricted to scholars of exceptional attainment in classical studies. When Pang-gyŏng was in his mother's womb, his mother repeatedly dreamed of ingesting clouds and mist, and said, "Essences of clouds are constantly entering my nose and mouth. Surely the child I am carrying was sent to me by the gods and Buddhas." Indeed,

Pang-gyŏng seemed to be a deity incarnate. Like his father, he was solemn, firm of character, unyielding in his observance of the law, and his presence was as calming as it was commanding. During the years of Mongol depredation, he was the executive officer of the military commission in the northwest. On Kanghwa Island he had noticed huge tracts of potentially arable land rendered barren by the incursion of seawater; he built dikes and transformed the land into bountiful fields. Because the island lacked wells, the inhabitants had to cross the channel to carry water from the mainland, and many were captured by Mongol troops. Pang-gyŏng dug pools to capture the abundant rain, thereby providing the island with a regular supply of water. After King Wŏnjong's accession, he withdrew from active military service and devoted himself to the duties of a minister of state.

Following the royal succession, Im Yŏn despatched a trusted retainer, Kwak Yŏp'il, to the Mongol court to deliver a letter purportedly written by King Wŏnjong, stating that a lingering illness had prompted him to yield the throne to his younger brother, Prince Ch'ang.

On July 21, a delegation of six Mongol emissaries, Urudai among them, arrived in Kangdo with the two Japanese, whom Kubilai had ordered the government of Koryŏ to return to Tsushima. The government selected Kim Yusŏng and Ko Yu to escort the two Japanese, and also to present the Japanese with the state paper which the previous Mongol embassy to Japan had failed to deliver. This would be the fourth instance of Koryŏ's despatching envoys to Japan.

The party of Koreans and Japanese left Kangdo for Japan at the end of July. As before, the Ch'ojijin ferry point was thronged with well-wishers.

*

Toward the end of August, an emissary arrived from the Mongol Empire bearing an edict which stated, in effect: I have not been informed of any misdeed of King Wŏnjong; yet a royal succession was carried out without the permission of your suzerain; submit a report describing the circumstances in full.

When Kwak Yŏp'il was traveling to the Mongol court a month earlier he had encountered Crown Prince Sim at Yongju on the bank of the Yalu River. He was obliged to divulge the purpose of his mission to the crown prince, who was traveling homeward. Informed of the recent turmoil, Sim had hastened back to Yen-tu and appealed to Kubilai for help.

Im Yŏn begged Yi Chang-yong to go to the Mongol court to mollify Kubilai. But Yi explained, "I have never been favored by Kubilai. Not once during my previous audience did I see him smile. The consequence of that audience was Kubilai's ordering Koryŏ to build warships and mobilize troops. I urge you to send General Kim Pang-gyŏng instead. I have been told that Kubilai admires the general and has often praised him. Surely he would be inclined to trust him." Wishing to delegate this vital mission to Kim, Yi was determined to stay in Kangdo, at his king's side.

The court, therefore, bade Kim Pang-gyŏng to accompany the emissary back to the Mongol Empire with a letter of explanation similar to that which Im Yŏn had entrusted earlier to Kwak Yŏp'il. Kim Pang-gyŏng left Kangdo at the beginning of September. Kubilai's reply was delivered to Kangdo on November 11 by Ho-te: Wŏnjong, his younger brother Ch'ang, and Im Yŏn were to appear at the Mongol court so that Kubilai could himself question the three principals to his satisfaction and render judgment. The edict concluded with notification of a forthcoming movement of Mongol troops into Koryŏ:

. . . because powerful courtiers of your nation have wantonly effected a royal succession, I shall send Prince Torenka and others to Koryŏ to administer the affairs of your secretariat. I shall send troops eastward so that your country may be pacified. They shall be concerned only with your leaders and will not trouble other officials or your people. Inform your country that the tranquility it had enjoyed before shall be restored.

Yi Chang-yong's worst fears were about to be realized. The Mongols would use their military might to rectify Koryŏ's internal political affairs. Kubilai's intentions were clear. He would send his armies to Tung-ching or even further, to the border, where they would be held in readiness for an invasion. The despatching of Mongol troops could be avoided only by obviating the purported need for intervention. Wŏnjong must be returned to the throne. Yi contrived a plan. Im Yŏn surely knew of the threat he faced— he could not survive once the Mongol armies began to march. Although he was responsible for Koryŏ's crisis, his inflated self-pride would not permit him to accede to the urgings of his countrymen. Perhaps he would listen to the Mongol emissary. Yi would ask Ho-te to urge Im Yŏn to restore Wŏnjong's sovereignty.

Yi Chang-yong called at the state guesthouse on the palace grounds in order to meet with Ho-te. He had addressed a written plea to Ho-te as the latter was about to set sail for Japan three years earlier. Although they had merely exchanged nods of mutual recognition, Yi had come to feel a fondness for the portly Mongol whose poised manner set him apart from his fastidious, suspicious compatriots. Ho-te should have been punished for failure to fulfill his mission but had somehow managed to be exonerated, and he continued to visit Koryŏ periodically in his capacity as Kubilai's emissary. He had again been appointed the Mongol ambassador to Japan, and his visits coincided regularly with times of crises in Koryŏ. Of the many Mongols who came to Kangdo, he knew Koryŏ and its people best.

Having explained the purpose of his call, Yi Chang-yong asked Ho-te to help the nation weather yet another crisis. Ho-te said he would offer help, then promptly directed the conversation onto another course. Being a Mongol, he said, he was unable to judge Korean individuals on the basis of physical appearance and deportment; therefore he had studied the country and learned to distinguish among general types.

"A man from the northeast (Hamgyŏng province) is a dog that fights in a muddy field," Ho-te began. "A man from your northwest (P'yŏngan province) is a fearsome tiger emerging from a forest, a man from Kyoju (Kangwŏn province) is a stone Buddha set at the foot of a cliff, and a man from Sŏhae (Hwanghae province) is an ox that plows a field of rocks.

"A man from Kyŏnggi may be likened to the mirrored reflection of a beautiful woman," he continued thoughtfully, "and a man from Ch'ungch'ŏng province to a refreshing breeze on a night of the full moon. A man from Kyŏngsang province is a promontory of a large mountain, a man from Chŏlla province is a slender willow set to swaying in the spring breeze.

"The recently assassinated Kim Chun was a native of Sŏhae. He was quite the ox that plows a field of rocks. Im Yŏn is from the northwest—truly a fierce tiger that emerged from the forest to chastise Kim Chun and dictate the royal succession. Kim Pang-gyŏng, from Kyŏngsang province, is a promontory of a large mountain—a man who may well be the cornerstone of your country. You, honored chief minister, were born in Kyŏnggi—a beautiful woman reflected in a mirror!" He laughed heartily.

In spite of his tendency to banter, Ho-te seemed to be a man of surpassing wisdom. He had taken stock of the people of Koryŏ. His comparing Yi Chang-yong to "a beautiful woman reflected in a mirror" may have been his way of suggesting that Yi had commendable intentions but, regrettably, lacked the vigor to carry them out. He had resorted to a metaphor to criticize Yi's failure to prevent the forced abdication of King Wŏnjong. The metaphor might well have been expanded into an accusation: if Yi had executed Im Yŏn at the onset of the rebellion, he would not be begging for help now.

"I am embarrassed to have my nature described by so apt a comparison," Yi said. "But let me promise this. If King Wŏnjong regains the throne, I will flog my aged body to take myself to your distant nation and seek His Imperial Majesty's counsel on ways to restore my country's fortunes. Having received a summons from His Majesty, my king will soon present himself at the court of your emperor. I ask that you favor him with your good offices when that day comes, for I fear that neither I nor Kim Pang-gyŏng, that 'promontory of a large mountain,' will be at his side."

On November 23, very likely as a result of Ho-te's urging, Im Yŏn removed Prince Ch'ang from the throne and restored King Wŏnjong's sovereignty. Four days later, Yi Chang-yong left Kangdo to advise Kubilai that Wŏnjong was again Koryŏ's king, and would soon come to Yen-tu to pay him homage. Yi was on a mission far more important than those which had taken him to the Mongol

Empire twice before. He had now to inform Kubilai of Koryŏ's return to the status quo, thereby preventing Torenka's army from marching into Koryŏ. Even a day's delay might be consequential. It was essential that Kubilai rescind Torenka's orders.

Continuous travel through several days and nights brought the aged chief minister to northern Koryŏ, where an uprising had recently taken place. The royal court at Kangdo had known that one Ch'oe T'an, scribe for the northwest regional military command, had raised a standard of rebellion, proclaiming his intent to fight his way to Kangdo to chastise Im Yŏn. The court had sent an army to quell the insurrection, then paid the matter no further heed because Ch'oe T'an was reported to have gone into hiding.

What Yi Chang-yong learned about the rebel appalled him. Aided by one Yi Yŏnnyŏng of Samhwa prefecture, Ch'oe T'an had gained control of three prefectures in the northwest with surprising swiftness. He had murdered the governor of Hamjong, banished the commander of Tando, an island near the estuary of the Taedong River, and captured and executed the commander of Sŏgyŏng. He then led his army northward, striking swiftly at the walled cities of Yongju, Yŏngju, Ch'ŏlju, Ŭiju, and Chaju; but after executing their governors, he had abruptly suspended military action. His whereabouts unknown, he remained a silent but pernicious presence throughout the region. Although Ch'oe T'an had declared his intention to chastise Im Yŏn, it might have been merely a ruse to gain popular support. Yi Chang-yong now knew that this was no ordinary insurrection.

As he approached Sŏgyŏng, he saw written notices, posted in every village he passed, predicting the imminent arrival of an imperial Mongol army entrusted with the mission of lifting the local populace out of the degrading abyss of poverty: "Look forward to the arrival of the holy army." "Three thousand Tartar troops will cross the border in days." "An army of three thousand troops, on orders of the son of Heaven, is fast approaching the Yalu River." Although they varied in their wording, they conveyed the same ominous message. Kubilai's edict had mentioned the eastward movement of Prince Torenka's army, which had been ordered to restore tranquility in Koryŏ. It was a threat, to be sure, but the Mongol army was

not yet expected to violate Koryŏ's border. The widespread prediction of the Mongol coming was evidence of a regional conspiracy to
invite the incursion of the Mongol army. Without doubt it was
Ch'oe T'an's work.

Suddenly Yi Chang-yong was frightened. The two months since
Ch'oe T'an had gone into hiding in early October had passed in
uneasy silence. What else had the rebel done in that interval? North
of Sŏgyŏng, Yi saw similar notices posted in every village right up to
the bank of the Yalu River, but he saw no soldiers. All local Koryŏ
constabularies had vanished, and Ch'oe T'an's forces were nowhere
to be seen. Cities and villages appeared peaceful, their inhabitants
preoccupied with preparations for the oncoming winter's confinement. At every daily stop, Yi asked the residents what kind of
changes they were expecting. But he was disappointed, for no one
seemed to have paid attention to the notices proclaiming the coming of their "savior." He was told that local administrators and con-
stabulary forces had quickly abandoned their stations when Ch'oe
T'an rebelled; no one knew where they had gone. Government
offices and military billets stood empty. The populace in general
appeared to be uninterested in these changes. They were concerned
only with sustaining their livelihood.

Yi felt troubled as he embarked on a crossing of the Yalu River.
The ferry left Ŭiju and made its customary stop at an island in mid-
stream, the site of the walled city of Taebu, established during the
Liao Dynasty [907–1125]. What Yi learned at Taebu jolted him.
Ch'oe T'an had recently stopped there on his way to the Mongol
Empire and had met Tudur, who was traveling to Koryŏ as an emissary from the Mongol court. Tudur had abruptly turned back, and
Ch'oe T'an had also turned back. Yi Chang-yong's uneasiness
turned into alarm. Could Ch'oe T'an have sought Mongol intervention in order to retain the power he had acquired? Could he have
concluded a treacherous agreement with Tudur?

Yi turned these thoughts over in his mind time and again as the
ferry sailed away from the midstream island.

No! His shout was an involuntary denial of a growing apprehen-
sion. The surprised glances of his two dozen subordinates shot
toward him. Try though he might, Yi could not control the trem-

bling in his withered body. He sprang to his feet, but was held fast by his attendants. The ferry was now in turbulent waters. His glance fixed on the dark, murky surface of the flow, Yi tried desperately to clear his mind. Was Cho'e T'an now ceding the territory under his control to the Mongol Empire? The posted notices Yi had seen had nothing whatsoever to do with welcoming Mongol forces to assist in the chastisement of Im Yŏn. The inhabitants were being prepared to accept Mongol rule!

Yi Chang-yong burned with impatience as the ferry headed toward P'o-so-fu on the opposite shore. Surely, he thought, he could obtain reliable information once he was in Mongol territory. But the information he obtained in P'o-so-fu was hopelessly vague. There men of many races were preoccupied with cultivating minuscule plots of land amid an expansive wilderness, wholly unconcerned with presumed realities. The men of Yi's party took to their swaying mounts and, excluding brief stops for their midday meal, traveled on continuously from early morning to the deep of night. Yi's subordinates repeatedly urged him to stop, if only for one day to rest his weary body, but Yi would not heed them.

The party arrived in Tung-ching and found the city in chaos, its streets congested with soldiers and horses. Conspicuous in the eyes of the travelers were small groups of strollers who wore Mongol uniforms but were unmistakably of Korean extraction. Some of them appeared to be in active service, others to have been demobilized and set to wandering. In any case, they had been conscripted from the Koreans who had become Mongol subjects. The number of troops of Mongol extraction was considerable, surely much larger than the three thousand rumored to have been mobilized and encamped within the city. Among other rumors: Torenka, Chao P'i, and others had been assigned to Tung-ching as supervisors of the district secretariat and had already assumed their duties in the city; the army was commanded by a general named Hsiao Pu-hua; the real commander was not Hsiao Pu-hua, but General Mongkut; the resident commandant was at odds with Torenka and the others newly arrived, and separate orders covering all matters were being issued from two separate headquarters. In truth, no one seemed to know precisely who was in command of which military unit.

On the night he arrived, Yi heard that Kim Pang-gyŏng was also in Tung-ching, but he could not find him. Kim would have been able to advise him how he might best carry out his mission in Yen-tu. Yi left Tung-ching early the next morning. Arriving in Yen-tu on December 15, he went directly to Crown Prince Sim's quarters. He was surprised to see new lines etched on the prince's face. By speaking with the crown prince, Yi Chang-yong learned that the thought which had so frightened him as he crossed the Yalu River was quickly becoming a reality. Ch'oe T'an had presented the Mongols with an astonishing proposal: to surrender the land he controlled—a vast area encompassing the territories of the northern border and the western seas, containing sixty walled cities in all. Although Kubilai was said to have taken the proposal under consideration, Crown Prince Sim did not believe that he would accede to the wishes of a rebel. "Kubilai is a ruler who observes propriety," he said. Yi did not believe that. Kubilai held a large army in Tung-ching, poised to march, and he now had a pretext for invading Koryŏ: to chastise Im Yŏn for meddling with the kingship of a tributary state. He would not reject an offer of Korean land however much he might distrust Ch'oe T'an. But Yi did not divulge these thoughts to the crown prince. He feared that his dread might be prophetic.

Yi entered a request for an audience with Kubilai. Although he expected to be granted an audience immediately—for he had come as Koryŏ's emissary to report on King Wŏnjong's return to the throne—he was instructed instead to resubmit his request through the imperial secretariat. He complied, then waited uneasily. He learned that the huge Mongol army was still garrisoned in Tung-ching, that its march into Koryŏ had been halted as a result of Crown Prince Sim's appeal to Kubilai. Sim had been persuasive in pleading for a postponement of troop movements until his royal father arrived in Yen-tu.

Alone in an alien court, Prince Sim had been working to stave off the peril to his homeland. The proper order of royal succession had been restored, and King Wŏnjong would come to pay homage to Kubilai. If only Yi Chang-yong could testify to these truths, Kubilai would have no reason to send Mongol troops into Koryŏ. Yi had come to Yen-tu precisely to advise Kubilai of these recent developments, and he was frustrated by his inability to meet with Kubilai. If Kubilai were truly concerned over Koryŏ's internal dissension, he should have ordered Yi immediately into his presence. Although Prince Sim entered requests repeatedly on Yi's behalf, he was told that the Mongol emperor's preoccupation with affairs of state prevented his granting requests for audiences.

On December 19, King Wŏnjong left Kangdo with a retinue of seven hundred men. The Mongol envoy Ho-te accompanied the party. During the king's absence, the crown prince's younger brother, Prince Chong, would rule. Im Yŏn refused to join the royal entourage even though he had been summoned by Kubilai. He would excuse himself, he said, because King Wŏnjong's return to the throne had nullified the intent of the summons. Im Yŏn, of course, was afraid. No one dared to urge him strongly, for he commanded the famed Sambyŏlch'o Elite Corps, the special defense force of Kangdo, which alone among all Koryŏ armed units had never lost a battle with the Mongols. His scheme had been thwarted by Kubilai. He was now as dangerous and unpredictable as an injured beast of prey.

The first day's journey brought the royal procession to Kaegyŏng, where Wŏnjong spent a restless night. The following morning, he was surprised by the arrival of a Mongol emissary bearing a rescript from Kubilai. It was an unusual one, essentially a duplicate of what Kubilai had issued to the rebel Ch'oe T'an. It was Kubilai's means of informing Koryŏ officialdom of his response to Ch'oe T'an's petition:

> . . . I address this counsel to Ch'oe T'an, commander of the district of Kuju of the Koryŏ nation, and to soldiers and citizens of the fifty-four cities of the territory of the northern border and the six cities of the territory of the western seas. Ch'oe T'an recently presented me with this warning: "The Koryŏ rebel, Im Yŏn, has informed us that he will force our men and their wives and children to join his expeditionary force to the east, and that he shall inflict injury on those who disobey him." You men, recognizing the impropriety of Im's action,

did not succumb to his threat; you have chastised the rebels and clarified the principle of unity. Your righteous action deserves praise. I
have issued a rescript to Ch'oe. Others among you shall be dignified
with separate rescripts to be issued through the imperial secretariat.
Subjects mine, accept my will and redouble your loyalty to me.

King Wŏnjong regarded the rescript with disbelief. His hands
trembled as he read the document again. Before he had left Kangdo,
a courier from Yi Chang-yong had warned him that Ch'oe T'an
might seek Mongol help to retain his newly gained authority. But he
had taken little notice of the matter, for he could not believe that
Kubilai would accept a rebel's petition. Yet here before his eyes were
acceptance and commendation. This rescript was an imperial mandate issued to the people of the zone encompassing the sixty cities,
to new subjects dwelling in newly annexed land. Kubilai's promise
to issue protective ordinances through the secretariat was, to all
intents and purposes, a clarification of the chain of authority that
would bind his new subjects. The ultimate sentence, "Subjects
mine, accept my will and redouble your loyalty to me," was an
unambiguous exhortation by Kubilai, the ruler, to those people of
Koryŏ who were now his subjects.

Wŏnjong promptly composed the following letter, to be delivered before his own arrival at the Mongol court.

. . . Having received a wholly unexpected edict, I now stand be-
numbed, gazing wonderingly at the stars. Here, on the nineteenth,
having taken to travel, I find myself raging and thrashing about,
much like the bewildered beasts in the wilds. Recently, provincials in
my small nation gathered in our western capital, murdered many city
commanders, and, wishing to evade punishment, used silken words
to deceive your honored court. Be informed of the true situation by
my emissary who will precede me, and decide whether the rebels'
actions are just or unjust. With your divine wisdom and your capacity
to protect and pity, forever allow my nation to remain a nation, never
to lose her people, who would serve you faithfully for myriad genera-
tions. This, indeed, is my wish. . . .

The tone of what he had written seemed reproachful. Wŏnjong
made several attempts at revision, but every change seemed to

increase the sharpness of tone he wished to eliminate. In the end, he decided to send what he had first drafted.

Ho-te offered to accompany the advance courier. He was aware of Wŏnjong's plight, and he wished to volunteer his good offices. Although Emperor Kubilai was his sovereign, Ho-te thought that his rescript needlessly debased Koryŏ.

King Wŏnjong's entourage left Kaegyŏng on the twenty-first. It began to snow that day, and the snowfall continued. The seven hundred travelers were strung out in single file as they trudged northward, a long, dark line etched against the whiteness of the plain. Although their progress was hampered by deep snow, they arrived in Sŏgyŏng on the twenty-seventh. By then, Wŏnjong had regained some calmness of mind. He began to think that Kubilai might have issued that rescript as a means of chastising him for not responding promptly to the imperial summons. Once before, when Kubilai sent wrathful messages accusing him of failure to fulfill the obligations of a tributary state, Wŏnjong had described Koryŏ's plight in fine detail and pleaded for a postponement of the date to deliver tributary goods—whereupon Kubilai promptly relented. Surely if he disclosed the truth and pleaded in all earnestness, Kubilai would again relent.

Reflecting over recent events, King Wŏnjong realized that he had to share the blame. Kim Pang-gyŏng had been despatched to the Mongol court to advise Kubilai of the recent royal succession. But Kim technically was Im Yŏn's emissary, not his. Kubilai would declare any message delivered by Kim to be an unacceptable justification of Im Yŏn's action. Yi Chang-yong was subsequently despatched to report on the king's return to the throne. But Kubilai had never liked Yi. All things considered, Yi was not an appropriate choice. His own son, Crown Prince Sim, had left for the Mongol court before Im's coup and knew little about the recent occurrences. Of all Koreans, he, Wŏnjong, was the one for whom Kubilai had shown fondness and trust. If he had hastened to Kubilai instead of those others, the crisis Koryŏ now faced would not have arisen. His inability to do so had brought Koryŏ misfortune. But he still had time. Despite having issued such a provocative rescript, Kubilai had not sent a single troop into Koryŏ.

"We have fought each other, but that time is now part of the past. Henceforth our two nations will surely be joined in friendship and abide in peace as members of one family." Kubilai had spoken those words. Wŏnjong had never forgotten the warmth of Kubilai's expression at their first meeting ten years before. Every word Kubilai spoke and the emotion he felt as he listened remained vivid in his memory. The travelers arrived in Pakchu on the bank of the Ch'ongch'on River on the last day of the year. There the king received couriers sent by Yi Chang-yong and Kim Pang-gyŏng. The couriers had come from Tung-ching and this puzzled the king, for Yi and Kim should have been in the Mongol capital. Nevertheless, he was over-joyed by the prospect of seeing them before meeting with Kubilai in Yen-tu.

When he read the letters from Yi and Kim, the king understood why those messages had been entrusted to vassals of the highest rank. The letters spoke of exceedingly grave matters: Yi Yŏnnyŏng, an accomplice of Ch'oe T'au, had implored Kubilai to send Mongol armies across the border into Koryŏ; Kubilai would despatch General Mongkut at the head of two thousand troops and authorize the supervisor of the district secretariat in Tung-ching to order Mong-kut's army into action; Mongkut was prepared to invade Koryŏ; the king must send a courier to Kubilai right away in order to forestall this action.

Wŏnjong that night composed a memorial to Kubilai. Lamps were lit far into the night in the room of the monastery that served as the royal quarters, and men were seen coming and going fre-quently. Consulting with his three principal vassals, Wŏnjong at first composed a memorial to Kubilai, then recast it into a petition addressed to the imperial secretariat.

. . . I have learned that Ch'oe T'an and other rebels of my small nation have entreated your honored court to despatch two thousand imperial troops to protect territory which they say is threatened by Koryŏ's troops. I have also learned that His Imperial Majesty's wish regarding this matter has been conveyed to your office. The truth may easily be discerned. Although I knew about the rebellion, I refrained from chastising the rebels for they had surrendered them-selves to your honored court. I am now on the road of travel. Who among my vassals would dare lead troops into aggressive action dur-ing my absence? Could you not refrain from despatching your troops until I have had the opportunity to speak in his imperial presence? Would you now send troops into my territory, only to terrify my sub-jects? I implore you, honored secretary, to convey the purport of this petition to His Imperial Majesty; I implore you to recognize my loy-alty and my son's loyalty to His Majesty, and to favor us with your protection.

Thus was King Wŏnjong preoccupied on the last day of 1269, a hectic, troublesome year. Soon the new year dawned, the eleventh since his enthronement. The king sent a party of twelve riders to deliver his petition to the district secretariat in Tung-ching, then held the briefest of formal festivities to welcome the new year, and departed with his entourage for Yen-tu. Snow fell continually but sparsely, maintaining a thin mantle over the plain, and the cold wind stabbed without mercy into the flesh of the riders. On the fifth, the king divided his entourage into two contingents, himself leading an advance party consisting of one hundred of his hardiest men. The other six hundred would follow them to Tung-ching and remain there, awaiting the king's return from Yen-tu.

At dusk on January 9, two parties of riders approached each other on the desolate, snow-covered plain. Yi Chang-yong, Kim Pang-gyŏng, and some forty others were riding out from Tung-ching to greet their king. They lined up in two rows and, when King Wŏn-jong's party had ridden through, fell in behind the column. Yi and Kim sped their mounts and took positions behind the king, who promptly ordered them to pull up alongside him. The three rode on silently. Yi had left Kangdo on November 21, more than forty days before. Kim had left Kangdo in June and had not seen the king in six months. Each had much to say but neither knew where to begin.

King Wŏnjong at last broke the silence. "What must I do?" he asked.

"Ride quickly to Yen-tu and meet Kubilai," Kim said, wiping the snow from his face. "I do not think that all is lost."

"Can my meeting with him prevent the invasion?"

"An invasion would lead to the Mongol's annexing a broad strip along our northwest border," Kim replied. "Mongkut has his army poised to march. But he has not received his orders, for Crown Prince Sim has pleaded with Kubilai to wait until you arrive. Kubilai seems determined to send his armies into Koryŏ, but that would be aggression, no matter what his intent. If Your Royal Highness could meet with Kubilai and plead certain inviolable principles, surely Kubilai could not justify his action. He would have to revoke his orders. Who, after all, can insist that rivers flow upstream?"

Despite his tendency to mumble, Kim Pang-gyŏng, known for his lack of eloquence, stated his opinion clearly: Im Yŏn's coup d'etat and Ch'oe T'an's rebellion had given Kubilai the pretext he needed to invade Koryŏ; but Kubilai had not rejected Crown Prince Sim's plea outright, and so this crisis might yet be resolved if only King Wŏnjong could meet with Kubilai.

Yi Chang-yong remained silent. The king regarded his aged chief minister whose body seemed to have shrunk even further. Addressed by the king, Yi shook his head in disagreement.

"You must be prepared for the worst," Yi said. "Kubilai has an army ready to march into Koryŏ the moment you arrive in Yen-tu. Kubilai has been known never to change a decision he has made. Would he make an exception for our sake? He will distort reason as he sees fit. But you may rest assured that Koreans residing in the strip of land north of the Taedong River will remain steadfastly loyal to Koryŏ though their lands may be annexed by the Mongols. That territory is but a small part of Koryŏ. Even though Koryŏ might lose one-half, even two-thirds, of itself to invaders, so long as even an acre of land remains identified as the Koryŏ nation, all lost territories will eventually coalesce again into the Koryŏ we now know. Be prepared to expect the worst, but you must never despair."

"Chang-yong, are you weeping?" King Wŏnjong asked, for Yi's face was wet. Perhaps it was the snow.

"I have no reason to weep now. I shall save my tears for a time to come when I will have to weep." And he wiped his face with his hand, as Kim had done earlier.

Two days later, on the eleventh, Wŏnjong's entourage entered Tung-ching. All the streets within the city walls teemed with

Mongol soldiers and their horses. Camped outside the walls was an even larger army of horse-riding warriors. Both Torenka and Ch'ao P'i, who had been assigned to the district secretariat in Tung-ching, had brought their armies with them. So had Mongkut, who had been ordered to invade Koryŏ. Mongkut's army was far larger than the two thousand noted in Kubilai's rescript. The unit of Korean expatriates alone numbered more than two thousand, and was far exceeded in size by the contingent of Mongol troops.

Although Kim Pang-gyŏng had accompanied Torenka's army to Tung-ching in September, he had only a vague notion of its current strength. He said that units were constantly on the move, coming and going between Tung-ching and Yen-tu. He did not know why. The Mongol high command apparently planned to use Kim as a staff officer, and had ordered him to stay with Mongkut in Tung-ching. It seemed that Yi Chang-yong had been sent from Yen-tu to Tung-ching for a similar purpose.

King Wŏnjong left Tung-ching the next day accompanied by one hundred men. The district secretariat would not permit Yi and Kim to accompany the king. As Wŏnjong continued on to Yen-tu, that familiar destination seemed much farther away than he remembered. He was prodded by impatience as he thought of Crown Prince Sim anxiously awaiting his arrival. He continued to believe, as Kim did, that his meeting with Kubilai would resolve the crisis. He would not let himself be influenced by Yi's opinion of Kubilai; indeed, he knew he must not lest he despair.

In the afternoon of their fifth day out of Tung-ching, they encountered a Mongol unit coming from the opposite direction. It consisted of cavalry, foot soldiers, and transport troops leading horse-drawn carts. There was an air of urgency about the fast-moving army. No sooner was that unit out of sight than another appeared on the far horizon, to be followed by yet another large detachment. The Koryŏ travelers were compelled to yield the road as each of them passed by.

Late that night, the travelers came to a small village where they could take lodging. They learned from the village elder that the massive troop movement had been precipitated by orders sent to Mongkut, to lead his army promptly into Koryŏ. If that were true,

Mongkut's army had already left Tung-ching for Koryŏ. The armies that had marched past them would either be garrisoned in Tung-ching, replacing Mongkut's troops, or follow Mongkut's units into Koryŏ.

"Am I too late?" Wŏnjong asked himself. "Would Kubilai have issued such orders, knowing that I would be in Yen-tu within ten days? Could Kim Pang-gyŏng and I have been misguided?" Pondering such questions, Wŏnjong spent most of the night seated upright in a darkened room in the modest house that served as his quarters. He could only hope that the village elder had been mistaken.

His party left the village at dawn. That day as well, they encountered several more units marching in the opposite direction. The messenger he sent to each of the unit commanders brought back the same reply: "I have not been informed of our ultimate destination, but expect to receive final orders in Tung-ching."

The weather worsened, and on some days blizzards kept them off the road. Frequently, for the better part of a day, they were forced to yield the road to Mongol units. They at last approached Yen-tu on the last day of January, more than ten days late.

That morning an emissary from Kubilai came to King Wŏnjong, and the two met at a monastery in a small village near the fringe of Yen-tu. The emissary was Hong Tagu. Wŏnjong had last seen him ten years before, when he had come as a messenger bearing the news of Wŏnjong's father's death; he was then seventeen. In the intervening years, Hong had grown to sturdy manhood. He retained no traces of adolescence. With broad shoulders, large clear eyes, and a wide, intelligent forehead, he looked like an exemplary military commander. He spoke softly. Yet even more than before, his manner was cold.

The instant their eyes met, Wŏnjong knew that Hong Tagu again had unhappy news.

Hong Tagu brought an imperial rescript issued by Kubilai in his capacity as suzerain of Koryŏ. Having explained that this rescript had already been delivered to Kangdo, he placed a copy before Wŏnjong:

. . . Since my enthronement, I have taken pity on your country, so plagued with military disorder. Having helped solidify your kingship and withdrawn my army, for ten years I have been circumspect in my regard for the protection and safety of your country. Unhappily, the rebel Im Yŏn disturbed this tranquility, manipulating the kingship to suit his own wishes and daring to bestow the crown on the lord of An'gyŏng Prince Ch'ang. He continues to defy my order to present himself to justify his actions. How can I not chastise him? I have despatched the supervisor of the district secretariat to lead an army eastward. His only purpose is to chastise Im Yŏn. There is no intent to punish the lord of An'gyŏng Prince Ch'ang. He shall be treated with magnanimity. I am not aware of any other threat or suspicion requiring my investigation.

The rescript was dated January 17. After reading it, Wŏnjong respectfully raised the sheet above his bowed head, then returned it to the letter box. The rescript said clearly that an army had been despatched to chastise Im Yŏn, but it made no mention of the vast territory which Ch'oe T'an had surrendered to the Mongols. Did the incursion of that huge Mongol army have no purpose other than to chastise Im Yŏn?

Wŏnjong asked about Ch'oe T'an's known wish to surrender to the Mongols.

"His Imperial Majesty recognized Ch'oe's loyal intent and accepted his petition," Hong replied.

"And what did his petition concern?"

"The sixty cities in the territories of the northern border and the western seas."

"What is meant by the phrase 'accepted his petition'?"

"It means that His Imperial Majesty has permitted Ch'oe T'an to cede the land north of Chabi Pass to the Mongol Empire. Sŏgyŏng has been renamed Tongnyŏng-pu. An emissary has been despatched from Yen-tu to inform your government of this."

King Wŏnjong managed with extreme difficulty to maintain a posture of dignity. It was finished! An audience with Kubilai on the next day would serve no purpose. Impassioned pleas would be meaningless, for Mongol troops were already in Koryŏ and the territory north of Chabi Pass had been annexed. Hong Tagu, that harbinger of bane, quietly left Wŏnjong, who sat motionless, dazed.

King Wŏnjong arrived in Yen-tu that afternoon. Yi Chang-yong also arrived that day despite having left Tung-ching several days later than the king. When Mongkut's army marched away from Tung-ching, ostensibly to chastise Im Yŏn though in reality to seize north-west Koryŏ, Kim Pang-gyŏng had been ordered to accompany that army. For some reason—perhaps advanced age and poor health—Yi had been left behind to select his own course of action. He had promptly come in pursuit of his king. Through the good offices of the imperial secretariat, King Wŏnjong was provided with quarters on the palace grounds while his vassals were given lodging at Buddhist monasteries in the northwest sector of the capital.

On the second of February, King Wŏnjong was granted an audience with Kubilai in the great hall of the palace. Yi Chang-yong and several other principals of the party were also permitted into the imperial presence. The meeting was largely ceremonial, and quite brief. Although Kubilai asked about Im Yŏn's manipulation of Koryŏ's kingship, the topic seemed to hold little interest for him. He listened as each of the Koreans spoke, then nodded when each had finished. Wŏnjong reported that he had resumed the kingship and had devised tentative solutions to the difficulties besetting his kingdom, and again Kubilai merely nodded. He urged Wŏnjong to convey any wishes he might have to the imperial secretariat. He repeated this, and then added that Wŏnjong should not hesitate to declare his every wish.

On this occasion also, Wŏnjong did not feel as if he were in the presence of a cruel monarch. Although he knew that Kubilai had ordered the ongoing invasion, certainly a flagrant breach of justice, he wondered if the aggression had not been precipitated by some mistake. Perhaps events would reverse themselves, and conditions would eventually revert to those before the invasion. He felt compelled to indulge in wishfulness. Perhaps everything he sought would be granted if he were to petition the secretariat as Kubilai had urged. The warmth of Kubilai's expression, of his total aura, was unchanged. The only difference Wŏnjong noticed was his tendency now to dwell in ruminative silence. Wŏnjong was then fifty-two and Kubilai fifty-six, but in no one's eyes did Wŏnjong appear to be the younger. He had aged quickly, far beyond his actual years. Kubilai, looking far younger than his years, brimming with vigor, seemed the personification of authority.

Back in his quarters after the audience, King Wŏnjong shared his thoughts privately with Yi Chang-yong: he wished to petition the secretariat for the return of the sixty cities; indeed, he felt compelled to do so, hoping that it might in some way benefit Koryŏ. But he did know how to proceed and therefore needed Yi's counsel. Yi reminded the king of the ineptness of his previous counsel. Under no circumstance, he had predicted, would Kubilai send his armies into Koryŏ until King Wŏnjong had met with him in Yen-tu. But Kubilai had ordered the invasion knowing well that Wŏnjong would soon be in Yen-tu. Perhaps men who rely on force had to resort to duplicity as a tactical device—it would be pointless pleading with such a man to give back land that was already his. Kubilai coveted not only those sixty cities, but all of Koryŏ.

Yi paused for thought, then suggested a course of action that might possibly work to their advantage: confuse the Mongol policy-makers by voluntarily offering to do what they intended to force upon Koryŏ; let them know that we wish to be accepted as a subject state in name as well as in substance, that we are willing to place our fate entirely in their hands.

"We have two ways to make our wish known," Yi said. "On the crown prince's behalf we can seek the hand of a Mongol princess in marriage. If such a marriage is approved, Crown Prince Sim would enter into a filial relationship with Kubilai, and I doubt that even Kubilai would force outrageous demands on his own son-in-law. Also, we can ask the Mongols for a contingent of troops to assist in moving our capital back to Kaegyŏng. By seeking Kubilai's help to relocate our capital, we should be able to convince him of the sincerity of our wish to be subservient. Kubilai might then view the matter of our sixty northwestern cities in a different light. These are the only clever ideas that occur today in my aged, feeble mind."

The crown prince was agreeable to the plan suggested by Yi. That night, Prince Sim and Yi wrote the petition to be submitted to the Mongol secretariat. Yi felt unusually troubled as he attempted to compose sentences. He no longer had any confidence whatsoever in his own ideas or ability.

On the fourth, the petition was delivered to the imperial secretariat. A few days later, King Wŏnjong submitted a second petition, requesting the reversion to Koryŏ of the sixty northwestern cities. Then they waited.

Two days had passed when the lord of Yŏngnyŏng Prince Chun and Hong Tagu came to Wŏnjong's quarters with Kubilai's reply to both petitions. A curious pairing, the men from Koryŏ thought. Hong Tagu's father was executed because Prince Chun had slandered him. Chun therefore would be Hong Tagu's mortal enemy. Although they now shared the post of senior military and civil administrator of expatriate Koreans, their dislike for each was easily discernible. Hong sat to one side, deferring to Prince Chun, who assumed the role of Kubilai's surrogate.

"The laws of Tartars, too, recognize the legitimacy of marriage as a means of conjoining clans. If a request for such a union were truly sincere, would it not merit compliance? However, you came to this country with a different purpose in mind. Should you not return to your country immediately so that your people may be consoled? The matter of our Imperial Princess does not merit discussion at this time."

Three men of Koryŏ—King Wŏnjong, Crown Prince Sim, and Chief Minister Yi Chang-yong—were present to hear those words. The king and the crown prince listened with heads slightly bowed. Yi, burning with humiliation and anger, kept his gaze fixed on Prince Chun. He might have endured this travail had those words been uttered by Kubilai, but not when they issued from the mouth of a Korean. He smarted at his own imprudence. Kubilai had no reason to award his daughter's hand to the Korean crown prince. His plan to subvert Koryŏ was working well, and he had no need to make concessions.

Hong Tagu then stood up to assume the role of spokesman. Whereas Chun had spoken on Kubilai's behalf, Hong Tagu merely conveyed information; and he spoke with a measure of courtesy.

"His Imperial Majesty immediately approved your request to the secretariat for military assistance. Torenka will soon be despatched with an army that will serve as rear guard to Mongkut's."

Yi felt the blood draining from his face. Whereas they had sought Mongol assistance to facilitate the moving of the capital, Kubilai was about to send in an army to occupy Kangdo!

"And regarding the other matter?" Yi asked in King Wŏnjong's stead, referring to the request for the return of the sixty cities.

"I understood that there were no other matters requiring discussion," Hong replied.

"We thank you for having assumed an arduous mission," said Yi. "Your message has raised some questions in our minds. We shall petition His Imperial Majesty again." He rose quickly from his chair, wishing to banish Hong Tagu and Prince Chun from his sight.

The instant the visitors left, Yi Chang-yong prostrated himself before the king and the crown prince and begged forgiveness for having offered counsel that would bring injury to their country.

"I doubt that Emperor Kubilai has personally read our two petitions," King Wŏnjong said after a stretch of silence. "If he had, this could not have happened."

Prince Sim quickly agreed. Yi could not, for he believed that all that had happened was unmistakably the working of Kubilai's will.

On the following day, Wŏnjong sent the Mongol emperor a petition requesting the revocation of the orders despatching Torenka's expedition and asking, instead, for the assignment to Koryŏ of a *darughachi,* or civil administrator: ". . . Should two great armies follow one upon the other into my country, my people will be alarmed and will flee their lands, and I fear my inability to restrain them. I implore you not to activate the second army, and to keep the first army garrisoned in Tung-ching, away from the border."

He received no reply. On the twelfth, however, King Wŏnjong and Crown Prince Sim were invited to the palace. They were guided down long open corridors and through several gates, from the last of which a length of carpeting extended straight to Kubilai's throne. Although a thick mantle of snow lay upon the city, there was no snow within the palace enclosure. Archers and spearsmen in armor lined both sides of the carpeted strip. The One Hundred civil and military officials, clothed in fine ceremonial robes signifying rank and position, stood three abreast in a column stretching across the inner palace ground and into the great hall of state. Never before had Wŏnjong and his son met with Kubilai in such a grand, formal setting. In their eyes that day, Kubilai seemed suddenly grown into a man of colossal proportions.

Kubilai, in an unusually expansive mood, kept a smile on his face as he spoke, but neither the king of Koryŏ nor his son could keep his eyes fixed on him, for his presence dazzled them. Helplessly they lowered their gazes. Kubilai bestowed gifts on Wŏnjong and bade him return to Koryŏ, escorted by Torenka. Neither King Wŏnjong nor Prince Sim spoke during the audience. Wŏnjong had spoken freely with Kubilai before, and wished to again, and he was puzzled by his inability now to speak in the imperial presence.

CHAPTER 4

On February 17, King Wŏnjong left Yen-tu with his retinue of one hundred men. Crown Prince Sim and Yi Chang-yong were returning to Koryŏ with him. It snowed steadily as it had during the king's journey to the Mongol capital, but added to the elements was a strong gale. The excitement of hurried travel had dulled the king's sensitivity to misery as he hastened to Yen-tu a month earlier. Now homeward bound, subdued, he was tormented by the cold. The details of earth and sky were brushed over a solid white expanse, broken here and there by the blue glints of unfrozen patches of water.

On the fifth day of travel, they came to a walled city where a familiar Buddhist monastery loomed in prominence. There King Wŏnjong became feverish and took to a sickbed. The travelers would remain there until the king recovered. Although they were troubled by anxiety, they knew that Prince Chong would rule Kanghwa well in their absence. Because Mongkut's army was now in Sŏgyŏng, they did not think Im Yŏn would again contemplate treachery, for a display of treachery now would destroy him.

There was no joy in returning home. The sixty cities of northwest Koryŏ now belonged to the Mongols. At Tung-ching they would be turned over to Torenka, to be escorted home by his army. Torenka's army would probably remain in the vicinity of Kaegyŏng and Kanghwa. They doubted that the army would be withdrawn after the relocation of the capital. Judging from Kubilai's past actions, they could expect it to stay on indefinitely as an army of occupation.

Although the king's condition improved after two or three days, Yi Chang-yong favored moderation and persuaded the king to wait

a few more days before resuming travel. One night Yi dreamt of Im
Yŏn, his body lifeless, his back covered with boils. It was unmistakably a dream, but after it had ended Yi dwelt for some time in that
vague state between dreaming and wakefulness. Im Yŏn's second
son, Yumu, had appeared first in Yi's dream, begging him to bestow
the title of assistant privy councilor posthumously on his father, and
to appoint him to the post of special commissioner for policy formulation. Yumu then led Yi into the next room, and there Yi saw
Im Yŏn lying prone—he was dead.

Yi Chang-yong lay awake in a room faintly lit by the dawn, won-
dering. If Im Yŏn were indeed dead, that death would inspire con-
fused emotions in him. Im's manipulation of Koryŏ's royal succession had brought about the present crisis, and the death of a man
who had become a curse to Koryŏ should have been cause for rejoicing. Yet somewhere in Yi's heart dwelt a heaviness, a fusion of anger
and sadness perhaps, which one might feel as one pondered the fate
of a sacrificial victim. He had felt such heaviness of heart when Kim
Chun was assassinated, and once before that when the leaders of the
Ch'oe clan, which had wielded power before Kim Chun's rise, were
slain. Those men had commanded the Sambyŏlch'o Elite Corps,
the special troops that defended Kanghwa Island. With an inflated
regard for the strength of the corps, they had intimidated the overwhelming majority of the courtiers, who wished to submit to the
Mongols in order to save Koryŏ's monarchy; and they had refused
to abandon the unrealistic strategy of depending solely on the protection offered by Kanghwa's insularity. Ultimately each did injury
to his country by striving to perpetuate his own power and authority, blind to other consequences; but these facts alone did not fully
explain Yi's curious state of mind.

Im Yŏn's death was an occurrence in a dream. Yi could not know
if the dream had depicted a reality. "If indeed he has died . . . " he
muttered hopefully. With Im Yŏn dead, the opposition to moving
the royal court from Kanghwa would dissipate, and so too would
the justification for Torenka's occupation of Koryŏ. The king would
have a good reason to ask Kubilai to rescind the orders that would
send Torenka's army into Koryŏ. Dwelling in such rumination, Yi
could not but hope that his dream was a portent.

They made their departure three days later, but after another two days' travel they were compelled to stop at a small isolated village on a snow-covered plain. King Wŏnjong again took to a sickbed. Yi persuaded the king and Prince Sim to contain their anxiety—nursing the king back to health was their chief concern. After a sojourn of more than ten days, they left in fair weather, only to stop after another day's travel at the next village, where they rested for three more days. If they maintained this slow pace of travel, Prince Sim complained, the long winter would be over by the time they reached Kanghwa. Yi replied that their concern for the king's health gave them no alternative.

Yi Chang-yong fretted over King Wŏnjong's state of health, but not over the slowness of travel. Eagerly he awaited a courier from Kangdo who would bring them news of Im Yŏn's death. His dream had been too vivid. As the days passed, wish gradually became belief. Im Yŏn must be dead! And surely a courier would deliver news of his death to Tung-ching by the end of March. If that report were already in the hands of the Tung-ching district secretariat when they arrived there, they could then address a another plea to Kubilai to keep Torenka's army from crossing the border. When at last they arrived in Tung-ching, it was April 10. They had spent more than fifty days in travel since leaving Yen-tu.

No courier had come from Kangdo. The moment Yi Chang-yong knew this, he was able to clear his mind of the delusion that had preyed upon it. A unit of Torenka's army marched out of Tung-ching just as King Wŏnjong's party arrived. Two days later, the remaining units followed, deployed so as to provide front and rear guards for Wŏnjong's retinue, which was rejoined by the six hundred men who had stayed behind in Tung-ching. The soldiers were well armed. Although the ostensible purpose of this troop movement was to provide safe escort for King Wŏnjong, the imposing display of might was hardly consonant with the army's stated role.

On the twenty-eighth, the travelers took to boats on the Yalu River, touched briefly at Taebu City on an island midstream, then resumed the crossing which formerly would have brought them home. But the opposite shore and the land beyond it were now under Mongol jurisdiction. King Wŏnjong, his son, and Yi Chang-yong gazed vacantly at the dark surface of the flow; none of them spoke. Their vessel was in a line of dozens of war vessels, each following closely on the one before, filled to capacity with Mongol troops.

At the beginning of May, they approached Sŏgyŏng, which had been renamed Tongnyŏng-pu and was occupied by the army of Mongkut, who had been commissioned the emissary for Koryŏ's pacification. The army appeared to be at least twice the size of the declared two thousand.

When they came to a point within a day's journey of Sŏgyŏng, Torenka said he wished to consult King Wŏnjong concerning a message he intended to forward to Kanghwa. Although he had said "consult," Torenka dictated the message in his capacity as director of the Tung-ching district secretariat. On May 6, Torenka's subordinate Checheto and a Koryŏ general, Chŏng Chayŏ, were despatched to Kanghwa with a message enjoining Im Yŏn to present himself at the court of the Mongol emperor. Wŏnjong and his retinue remained billeted with Torenka's army, waiting for the couriers to return. Checheto and General Chŏng Chayŏ were back on the eleventh. They reported that Im Yŏn had succumbed to an illness on February 25, and his son, Yumu, had assumed his father's title and position.

What Yi Chang-yong had seen in a dream had actually occurred. Prince Chong, ruling in place of King Wŏnjong, had despatched an emissary on March 7 to report this event to the Mongols. Yi's prediction had been correct, except that the courier had failed to stop at Tung-ching.

General Chŏng Chayŏ reported that no one had raised objections to a separate royal rescript issued by King Wŏnjong to inform his subjects in Kangdo of the contemplated relocation of the capital. The rescript had stated:

His Imperial Majesty has commanded the director of the district secretariat Torenka, Chao Pi, and others to provide me with an armed escort. He bade me return to my country and convey to you these instructions which he has given me: "Should you return to your country and counsel your people, and should they all return to the former capital so that the quiescence of former days may be restored, then shall my armies be recalled. It goes without saying that any man who disobeys will be apprehended, and so will his wife and children. The departure from the island must not be conducted as on past occasions. Everyone, from civil and military officials on down to commoners in villages and hamlets, shall remove themselves along with their women and children.

"Furthermore, you shall send as tribute ten thousand piculs of newly harvested rice and also assist my armed units by supplying them with food and facilitating their overland movement. I am concerned lest witless people be astounded by the sight of a large belligerent army pressing up to your border. I urge you to counsel them promptly so that they may gain calmness of heart, rejoice in their labor, and receive my troops with generosity and hospitality."

Torenka's army struck camp to continue its march, and King Wǒnjong's party followed at a distance of a day's travel. On arriving at Yongch'on Station on the sixteenth, the king was informed by a courier from Kangdo that Im Yumu had been executed and commanders Yi Ǔngnyǒl and Song Kunbi had been exiled to a distant island. The courier did not know the reasons for these actions or who had initiated them. Yi Ǔngnyǒl and Song Kunbi, and certainly Im Yumu, had from the very beginning objected to the Koryǒ court's leaving Kanghwa Island, and so one could readily surmise that the forces that had opposed the capital's relocation had been eliminated in anticipation of King Wǒnjong's return.

On May 21, Torenka led his army into Kaegyǒng, then further on to Sungch'on-pu on the seacoast. He promptly sent a detachment of men to Kangdo to take Im Yǒn's wife and children captive. King Wǒnjong's party arrived in Kaegyǒng a day later. Convinced that the Mongol will must prevail, Yi Chang-yong advised the king that disorder could best be averted by removing the entire populace of Kanghwa Island to Kaegyǒng. On the twenty-third, King Wǒnjong issued a rescript to the residents of the island ordering the moving of the capital back to its former site.

The royal emissary returned from his mission and reported that the Sambyǒlch'o Elite Corps had declared its unequivocal objection to the relocation and, as a result, chaos had quickly overtaken the island; in several areas buildings had been fired as skirmishes took place.

On the following day, the twenty-fourth, more than one thousand island inhabitants came into Kaegyŏng with only the clothes they wore. Leaving the island, they said, was becoming increasingly difficult; bands of men, either renegades or Sambyŏlch'o corpsmen, were capturing residents who tried to leave from the usual ferry points on Kanghwa.

Again on the next day, an equally large number of escapees arrived in the capital. According to their reports, the elite corps had posted proclamations forbidding Kanghwa residents from leaving the island; those who had taken to boats with their families and possessions were being apprehended by elite corps troops manning war vessels. Although Torenka petitioned the Koryŏ court to call on the troops under his command to stabilize the situation, King Wŏnjong, Prince Sim, and Yi Chang-yong desperately forestalled the activation of his army, insisting on settling their own nation's affairs themselves. They pleaded that the elite corps, already restive, must not be provoked by an incursion of Mongol troops. The arrival of Torenka's great army in Kaegyŏng had doubtless ignited the elite corps' belligerence.

Yi Chang-yong posted a thousand men at various points along the coast to aid the escapees who were coming ashore day and night. The flames of beacons lighting the skies above both shores lent an unusual reddish glow to the Han River, and from the shore one saw the black outlines of vessels of all sizes racing one another, silhouetted against the dusky red surface.

In the early morning of the twenty-seventh, King Wŏnjong despatched General Chŏng Chayŏ across the channel to admonish the elite corps, and then repaired to the Munsu Monastery, establishing the royal court midway up the slope of Mount Munsu at a point overlooking the island stronghold. Shortly before noon, the royal consorts and ladies and their female attendants succeeded in escaping from Kanghwa and arrived at Sungch'on-pu. That afternoon, King Wŏnjong sent another emissary, General Kim Jidae, to meet with the elite corps, but the corpsmen ignored him. Torenka again pressed his wish to send his army into battle against the rebels, but Wŏnjong beseeched him for a stay of two days.

On the twenty-eighth, the king sent several more commanders to the island only to have them taken captive by the elite corps. The flame-lit clouds above the city of Kangdo could be seen from as far away as Kaegyŏng.

On the twenty-ninth, King Wŏnjong formally declared the Sambyŏlch'o Elite Corps disbanded. The situation on Kanghwa was beyond redemption, and the royal court of Koryŏ had chosen to dissolve the elite corps to prevent the outbreak of a calamitous disorder that would certainly follow on an invasion by Torenka's army. King Wŏnjong's edict was delivered to the island by an elite corpsman who had been take captive on the mainland. The royal edict was intended to have a divisive effect on the leaders within the corps.

The waters were unusually calm on the thirtieth, and numerous boats and ships seeking escape from the island made unobstructed crossings. All war vessels of the elite corps had suddenly vanished from the strait.

Those who escaped from the island on June 1 reported that General Pae Chungson had taken over the elite corps and pledged his loyalty to a monarch of his own choosing, the lord of Sunghwa Prince On (the elder brother of the lord of Yŏngnyŏng Prince Chun), who would establish a new royal court. The insurgents had become rebels against the throne.

On the following day, June 2, Torenka ordered three thousand of his troops to stand ready to invade Kanghwa Island. Vessels procured from coastal villages were grouped at approximately one dozen separate points of launch. King Wŏnjong no longer had a cogent reason to prevent Mongol troops from interceding.

On the third, Yi Chang-yong decided to cross over to Kanghwa together with Crown Prince Sim. Yi had not given up hope. Before the Mongols landed, he would meet with the staff officers of the elite corps in an attempt to prevent Koryŏ from descending deeper into chaos. Yi and Prince Sim sailed from Sungch'on-pu shortly before midday. Upon disembarking at Kanghwa's northern tip, they mounted steeds they had brought from the opposite shore and took to the road for Kangdo. They had brought only a few footmen with them lest the elite corps be alarmed by the sight of a large, ostensibly hostile group of men.

The settlements they passed through were deserted. Old men whom they occasionally encountered told them that everyone had fled into the forests because the Mongols intended to exterminate the island populace. A young man they saw lingering at the roadside told them a different story: the people had fled into the mountains, for the elite corps was forcing them all, men and women alike, to join them.

The inhabitants nearer the capital city, Kangdo, had not left their villages, but most of them were weeping in open displays of grief. All their young men had been forced aboard ships and taken southward along with the corpsmen. The air was filled with the wailing of women whose husbands and sons had been torn away from them.

The party entered Kangdo. They found the city changed beyond recognition. Every dwelling had been demolished, and household furnishings were strewn about the streets. Parts of the palace and the cluster of government office buildings had been reduced by fire and were still smoldering. A few Korean soldiers stood guard at the palace, and Prince Chong was safe, but the Diamond Vault had been broken into and the stored weapons taken. According to Prince Chong, General Pae Chungson and the elite corp night patrol instructor No Yonghui were the instigators of the rebellion; they had declared the lord of Sunghwa Prince On their king, appropriated arms from the Diamond Vault, distributing them among their troops, and early that morning had taken their possessions as well as government supplies on board ships and left Kanghwa Island. The vessels they had appropriated for their use, more than one thousand in number, formed a line touching stem to stern from Kup'o to Hangp'a River. Many of the wives and children of courtiers then in Kaegyŏng to welcome back their king had been abducted by the elite corps. Those who had opposed Pae Chungson had been executed—among them General Yi Paekki, the wife of General Hyon Munhyok, and the royal proctor Chong Mungam.

Yi Chang-yong despatched a messenger to Kaegyŏng, then sealed the Diamond Vault and had a reassuring proclamation posted throughout the island. He assigned men to gather and cremate the bodies of those who had drowned attempting to cross the strait.

The formal relocation of the capital from Kangdo to Kaegyŏng took place three days later. The sky above Kangdo that day was magnificently clear, but the bright expanse appeared curiously empty in the eyes of those who were leaving. Before the day ended Kangdo had become an uninhabited ruin. Had anyone remained he would have seen the early-summer winds raising swirls of dust on the deserted streets and flocks of crows settling to nest within the city walls. He would have noticed, too, that the roaring of the sea sounded nearer than it had before. By moving to Kaegyŏng the royal court had returned to the original capital, but it was an unwelcome move to a city that was no longer familiar.

In mid-June, while workers were laboring day and night to build temporary government offices and dwellings, Kim Yusŏng, who had left for Japan from Kangdo the previous autumn, returned with his party of seventy men. They entered Kaegyŏng by the South Gate, which had retained its name although it was merely the paved site of a gate tower that had been leveled by the flames of war. In the city they were stopped and questioned at posts manned by Mongol troops as they proceeded along the dusty main thoroughfare to the royal palace. Members of the mission were ushered into a large room in the temporary palace to partake of tea and sweets, but concern for the safety of their families disquieted them.

Kim Yusŏng met with King Wŏnjong and described his journey. The mission had arrived at Ina Bay on Tsushima Island on November 17. After a brief sojourn on the island, they had sailed to Kyushu and arrived at Dazaifu, western headquarters of the shogun's government. There they were given lodging in the constables' quarters. They waited until February for a reply from Japan's imperial court; but they received no reply and, perforce, returned home.

On King Wŏnjong's orders, Kim Yusŏng left the next day to present this information to Kubilai.

*

Having abandoned Kangdo and fled to the sea, the Sambyŏlch'o Elite Corps, its many valorous and meritorious accomplishments notwithstanding, was now no better than a horde of unruly rebels. The king could not ignore rebellion. On June 13, he sent an expedi-

tionary force commanded by the assistant privy councilor Shin
Sajŏn into Chŏlla province to subdue the rebels. Shin's army consisted of only one hundred men. As soon as Shin received reports of
elite corps troops landing in Chŏlla, he turned back to Kaegyŏng.
No one knew whether it was Shin's fear of the enemy that had sent
him into flight or whether he had refused to engage in battle his
comrades over the years, knowing well the resultant humiliation
that would be his. Shin Sajŏn placed himself in confinement and
refused to divulge the reason for his action. He was removed from
his post immediately.

The elite corps' enthroning of the lord of Sŭnghwa Prince On
and its issuing of royal pronouncements were unpardonable acts.
Yet those acts signified hostility to the Mongols, their oppressors,
rather than resentment of Koryŏ's monarchy. This hostility had
erupted suddenly, explosively. Excepting people whose families and
friends had been abducted or murdered by the elite corps, most
Koreans felt that those corpsmen had done what they themselves
might have done. They did not, of course, wish the elite corps
greater power, but neither did they wish it a destructive end. Pae
Chungson and other instigators might deserve the death penalty,
they thought, but the lives of the troops should be spared. Such also
were the sympathies of King Wŏnjong and Yi Chang-yong. But
Torenka's army would remain in Kaegyŏng until the rebels were
pacified; and, worse, the presence of rebels would give the Mongols
justification for sending more troops across the border.

In August the elite corps seized Chin Island and began to direct
their aggression at nearby provinces. Their strength increased with
each passing day—such was the news that reached Kaegyŏng. King
Wŏnjong appointed Kim Pang-gyŏng commander of the Chŏlla
Province Punitive Force, with orders to chastise the rebels. Kim had
remained with Mongkut's army in Sŏgyŏng, working behind the
scenes to keep that army from crossing the Taedong River. He had
served his country nobly. If, with Torenka's army already in Kaegyŏng, Mongkut's army had moved southward, the consequence
for Koryŏ would have been calamitous.

Kim Pang-gyŏng returned to Kaegyŏng as ordered and was ready
to leave that day at the head of the punitive force. Even a day's

delay, he feared, might prod Mongkut into action. Kim's army consisted of some sixty men, but the size mattered little. What mattered was the need to quell a rebellion in Koryŏ with Korean troops. He wished most of all to meet with the elite corps leader Pae Chungson and reason with him. Kim's fear was borne out by the declared wish of Ahai, who had replaced Torenka, to join the expedition against the elite corps in pursuance of Kubilai's orders. Koryŏ had no grounds for demurring.

In mid-September, Kim Pang-gyŏng and Ahai left Kaegyŏng at the head of an army of one thousand, designated a joint expeditionary force even though most of the soldiers were Mongols. Kim was understandably reluctant to participate in a conquest of men of his own race. Ahai, on the other hand, was simply engaging in the suppression of alien insurgents. From the start, therefore, a discord marred the relationship between the two commanders. The expeditionary force fought its way through Chŏnju, then routed the enemy in Naju and came to Samgyŏnwŏn, on the shore facing Chin Island, the stronghold of the elite corps. The chastising army won some of the skirmishes, and so did the rebels. Around this time, there were rumors that Kim Pang-gyŏng was carrying on secret negotiations with the enemy. In consequence, Kim was recalled to Kaegyŏng, but was returned to the front lines when the allegations were proven false. Such disagreeable incidents were perhaps unavoidable so long as a Mongol and a Korean, each harboring different sympathies, were in joint command of a common mission. Thus did the autumn of the year 1270—the seventh since the founding of the Mongol dynasty, the eleventh of King Wŏnjong's reign—rush by amid turbulence.

The Koryŏ government in Kaegyŏng received one report after another from the south describing victories over the elite corps. Whenever he read those reports, Yi Chang-yong wistfully entered into a state of thought likened to the soundless falling to the ground of leaves of the Chinese parasol tree. He savored the lyrical harmonies of a deepening autumn, but not the elation of receiving news of victories.

Unexpectedly, in December, this rescript was received from Kubilai:

Heed my thoughts. Japan has maintained amity with the Middle Kingdom since antiquity, and also has continued to communicate informally with your nation. Therefore, I once instructed you to despatch an emissary in order to inform those people of my sincerity and to urge them to submit to an amicable relationship. Because of the interference of officials stationed at their border, the Japanese court could not be advised of my will. The subsequent affair of Im Yŏn obliged me to postpone until now my good endeavor. Today tranquility again prevails in your country. I am despatching Chao Liang-pi as ambassador, and I anticipate his fulfilling his assigned mission. I have placed Kurimchi, Wang Kuo-ch'ang, and Hong Tagu in command of a contingent of troops that will escort the mission to the port of embarkation. They will remain in Kimju until the mission returns, and you shall provide for their needs. Have a fleet of vessels in readiness at Kimju for my emissaries. Let there be no display of neglect or parsimony.

Received along with the above rescript was a copy of this imperial admonition addressed to the king of Japan:

It is said that kingly men are not separated by boundaries. Already Koryŏ and my nation make up a single house. Your kingdom lies in close proximity to us. I despatched a mission to establish amity with your nation, but it was detained by your border officials at Dazaifu and not allowed to proceed further. Your two countrymen Tōjirō and Yashirō were comforted and returned to you with my rescript; but you have not replied. Although I wished to pursue this matter further, I could not because of the insurgence of Im Yŏn, a powerful courtier of Koryŏ. Was this also the reason for the failure of Your Royal Highness to send an envoy to my country? Perhaps you despatched an emissary whose travel was impeded. I could not know. Nevertheless, Japan has always claimed itself a nation that observes orthodox rites and ceremonies, and I would expect your subjects to observe the proprieties. Im Yŏn was recently executed, the monarchy of Koryŏ has been restored, and her people are again settled in tranquility. I have appointed the director of the archives Chao Liang-pi my ambassador and shall despatch him with papers to be delivered to you. If you should despatch your envoy, who would accompany my ambassador on his return, you would demonstrate your virtue and neighborliness. Such an act would bring you praise. Who would find pleasure in tolerating delays that would lead to a display of armed might? Your Royal Highness is enjoined to be circumspect in devising a response.

Having read the rescript, King Wŏnjong folded the sheet and raised it high in a gesture of respect, then replaced it in the letter box. It seemed as if a dreaded creditor, about whom he had forgotten while he attended to urgent matters, had not forgotten him and had suddenly reappeared at a precisely timed moment. Im Yŏn's manipulation of the throne, Ch'oe T'an's revolt, the annexation of the northwest territory, the arrival of Mongkut's army of occupation, the incursion of Torenka's army, the Sambyŏlch'o Elite Corps' insurrection, the relocation of the capital—it seemed as if a succession of troubling waves had broken on Koryŏ's shores since the year past, diverting his attention from the truly vital matter, and cresting in their wake was another wave, unimaginably huge and destructive. Wŏnjong waited until the Mongol emissary left, then handed the rescript to Yi Chang-yong, who made a slight gesture of honoring the sheet of paper before unfolding it.

As Yi finished reading the rescript, he was possessed by a desperation from which it seemed the only release would be in seeing Kubilai run through with a Korean sword. Given the opportunity, he would himself deliver the killing thrust, and such satisfaction that would bring! The torrent of emotion quickly receded.

"I am now seventy, too old to manage a crisis in our nation," Yi said, regaining his composure. "But I feel inspired to maintain good health and live as long as I can. Adversity tends to recur in greater numbers after a first occurrence. This is true of individuals and nations alike. But if the cause of one adversity is eliminated, the others tend to vanish in time. We must be patient and bide our time, and I shall live until we can look forward with certainty to brighter times. I sense an unusual purpose in Kubilai's sending a state paper to Japan. But we should not assume that this act will lead immediately to an attempt to conquer Japan. All will depend on Japan's reply. We of Koryŏ must do what we can to prevent the Japanese from provoking the Mongols."

Yi's expression hardened. "We must send our own envoy to

Japan," he said. "Our envoy must precede the Mongols'. We must inform the Japanese of the true intent of the Mongols. Once the Japanese know of Kubilai's determination and the power that his empire wields, surely they would exercise prudence. And we must quell the elite corps' rebellion, and do this quickly. Though we might, in some ways, be sympathetic to the aspirations of the elite corps, we cannot forgive their perpetrating a far-reaching rebellion to the great detriment of the country. If they cannot be quelled without Mongol assistance, then we must obtain that assistance. Eliminating civil strife is of paramount importance, and it must be done promptly. We cannot eliminate external threats while our own country is in disorder. The rescript spoke of a great army commanded by three generals crossing our border. We cannot prevent their coming. Surely that army will stay on for a protracted occupation of our land. What I fear most is the sight of those troops tilling our soil and settling on our land. We must not let that happen, but I do not know how we can prevent it. Unless we quell the rebellion promptly and thwart any Mongol attempt to conquer Japan, we shall forever live in fear of being colonized."

Even as Yi spoke, the king could perceive his lack of confidence. The actions he suggested might be futile. Kubilai wanted, above all, to station a permanent colonial army in Koryŏ. There was neither reason nor need to station a large Mongol army in south Koryŏ to await the return of their ambassador to Japan. One could readily discern Kubilai's scheme to attach the troops to the land, letting them till the soil to show that their presence need not be Koryŏ's burden, thus instituting a permanent occupation.

On December 2, Crown Prince Sim returned from the Mongol court, having reported on the relocation of the capital and the insurgence of the elite corps. Buha, a Mongol magistrate, accompanied Prince Sim back to Kaegyŏng.

"I have heard," said Buha, immediately upon greeting King Wŏnjong, "that a man who was implicated in the Im Yŏn affair continues to serve as a member of your court. He cannot be punished unless he is prosecuted." Clearly Buha was speaking of Yi Chang-yong. King Wŏnjong remained silent. Yi, seated in their presence, felt as though the very man he wished dead, Kubilai, had parried and now held him at bay.

"His Imperial Majesty doubtless believes that I should have met my death at the time of that incident," Yi said to him. "I could have chosen death, but I forbade myself that easy choice. I ask that you convey my statement to His Majesty."

On January 5 of the following year, 1271, King Wŏnjong relieved Yi of his post. Buha had come to Koryŏ with the specific purpose of seeing Yi Chang-yong expelled from the royal court, and Wŏnjong was obliged to submit to his wish.

Buha left for Yen-tu on the twelfth. His departure coincided with the arrival in Kaegyŏng of Chao Liang-pi, whose appointment as the ambassador to Japan had been noted in Kubilai's rescript. Chao was accompanied by the Mongol generals Kurimchi, Wang Kuo-ch'ang, and Hong Tagu, and an army of two thousand soldiers. King Wŏnjong and his vassals proceeded to the northern outskirts of the capital to greet them.

Kaegyŏng now bulged with Mongol troops. Residential dwellings, less than plentiful to begin with, were now wholly commandeered by the men of Ahai's army and the newly arrived troops. Torenka's army, which had come to Koryŏ to oversee the relocation of the capital, stayed on even though its task was finished; King Wŏnjong had considered protesting their continued presence. But the character of that army changed after Ahai replaced Torenka as its commander. With its three thousand men rotating regularly between the front lines and garrison duty in Kaegyŏng, it might well have been called the Elite Corps Punitive Force. Units of fighting troops returned north to Kaegyŏng constantly, and the southward egress of replacements was equally frequent.

Now, with the arrival of the army under the command of Kurimchi, Wang Kuo-ch'ang, and Hong Tagu, the transformation of Kaegyŏng into a Mongol military base was complete. The only Korean soldiers present were the fewer than one hundred assigned to guard the royal palace. Koryŏ's only effective defensive troops over the past decades, the Sambyŏlch'o Elite Corps, were rebels; the few loyal units stationed in the provinces could not be called up to the capital. Only after Ambassador Chao Liang-pi's arrival did the Koryŏ court learn that he would not be leaving for Japan until September. The newly arrived Mongol army had been ordered to station itself in the vicinity of Kimju and Happ'o during the interval between Chao Liang-pi's departure and return. Since Chao would not leave until September, that army had entered Koryŏ eight months before the beginning of its assigned mission and would remain on Korean soil until the following year. For all purposes, the Mongol army had taken full possession of the capital of Koryŏ.

On March 3, two emissaries, Hindu and Shih Shu, arrived from the Mongol court, bearing this rescript of Kubilai:

> I once despatched an ambassadorial mission to admonish the Japanese. Contrary to my expectations, the Japanese misguided themselves onto the path of insularity and failed to accept my benign admonition. You have known this. I am now intent upon establishing a commandery in Japan; I have entrusted an official with my rescript and despatched troops to settle on your land to become instruments for the advancement of my plan, for it is my wish to spare your country the burden of providing the services of an intermediary. I am therefore addressing this second rescript to you, to inform you beforehand of my expectations. With full willingness of heart and heedful consideration shall you support and assist in the implementation of my plan. You shall expect its success and thus shall your wish be in accord with mine.

Though subtly worded, the rescript announced the establishment of military colonies. What Yi Chang-yong had dreaded would now come to pass. The rescript stated, "I have . . . despatched troops to settle on your land." The emissaries Hindu and Shih Shu had been empowered to function as colonial administrators. Would the forces commanded by Kurimchi, Wang Kuo-ch'ang, and Hong Tagu become that colonial army, or would it be Ahai's army, still engaged in battle against the elite corps? Or would yet another army be sent into Koryŏ to fulfill that purpose? King Wŏnjong had a copy of Kubilai's rescript delivered to Yi Chang-yong, who had been living in confinement on the fringe of the city following his removal from office. He could not summon Yi, for Mongol officers were present daily at his court.

Yi sent his reply quickly:

> Do not let anything that may happen surprise you, for whatever may happen cannot be so implausible as to be beyond our human capabil-

ity to anticipate. All the events that have afflicted Koryŏ during the past several years should have been foreseen. Kubilai, too, is human. What his human mind can devise is limited. The establishment of a colonial army will probably be his last political design for Koryŏ. We cannot predict whether the Mongol units now in our country will become the colonial army or whether new units will be sent in. Whichever is the case, the ultimate difference will be negligible. Koryŏ will suffer greatly hereafter as the colonial troops exact commodities of all kinds from us; this is inevitable.

In addition to the infirmities of extreme age, my body has been ravaged by a succession of illnesses, each a cause of agony. Although I doubted my ability to endure the agony of an oncoming sickness, once I was afflicted with it I found the agony endurable—such is the nature of suffering. Endure you must, and so must the people of Koryŏ. And as you endure the harshness, pray accomplish two things. First, the expeditious suppression of the rebellion. The other being a matter concerning which I proffered counsel this past winter, I hesitate to restate it in a document that may remain a record. It must be done. Emperor Kubilai's scheme has at last emerged with clarity. Should he ever send forth an army of conquest, fate will bring to Koryŏ not mere suffering. It will bring extinction.

King Wŏnjong pondered that second imperative. He remembered Yi's hardened expression while saying, "We of Koryŏ must send our own envoy to Japan. Our envoy must precede the Mongols'." Although there was no assurance that sending such a mission would be successful, Wŏnjong decided to attempt it. It would be a dangerous act that would be considered a breach of faith; it would have to be carried out in secrecy, for its disclosure would bring disaster to Koryŏ and to King Wŏnjong himself. Chao Liang-pi's mission would very likely make a determination: whether or not the Mongol Empire should send forth an expedition to subjugate the Japanese. That determination would also determine Koryŏ's fate. Koryŏ must therefore avail itself of any means of influencing its own destiny. Should an army of conquest be sent to Japan, Koryŏ's fate, as Yi Chang-yong had warned, would be tantamount to extinction.

Several days after arriving in Kaegyŏng, the colonial administrators Hindu and Shih Shu presented King Wŏnjong with directives issued by the imperial secretariat detailing the Mongols' plan for colonization and the obligations to be incurred by Koryŏ. The two visitors proceeded to explain the contents: the office charged with overseeing the colonization, the colonial administration, would be located at Pongju, in the jurisdictional zone of Tongnyong-pu; colonies would be established at eleven locations, including Kaegyŏng, Pongju, Hwangju, and Kimju; furthermore, all Mongol units now stationed in Koryŏ would be subsumed under the colonial army.

King Wŏnjong caught his breath. By the most conservative estimate, Mongol soldiers stationed in Koryŏ numbered no fewer than six thousand. There was more: of the six thousand farm oxen needed by the colonial army, three thousand were to be provided by Koryŏ in exchange for compensation in silk; and Koryŏ was to supply all the farming implements, seed grain, fodder, and food required by the entire colonial army through autumn.

With great difficulty the king suppressed a gasp that had mounted in his throat. He must trust Yi Chang-yong's counsel, he told himself: man is a creature that can endure regardless of the extent and severity of his suffering.

King Wŏnjong immediately sent farming commissioners to the various provinces to establish a network for delivering plows and oxen to Pongju. He then sent the imperial secretariat a letter, its contents here summarized: Three thousand oxen is a quantity we shall have difficulty supplying. The orders having come from His Imperial Majesty, we shall not indulge in self-justification. We are profoundly grateful for the expressed intent of bestowing rolls of silk upon us in exchange. We have conferred with Colonial Administrator Shih Shu and with Kurimchi, Chao Liang-pi, Wang Kuo-ch'ang, and Hong Tagu. They have asked us to specify the quantity of oxen, plows, and seed grain that would be available for requisition. We have replied that we would be able to supply in advance of the farming season eleven hundred oxen, thirteen hundred plows, and fifteen hundred piculs of seed grain. We believe that the total number of oxen we can supply will reach two thousand before the end of this year. The quantity of plows and seed grain is less than what you have requested, but we shall endeavor to increase the quantities gradually to meet the stated figures. And we shall strive to our utmost to raise provisions in amounts your soldiers and horses would need to stave off hunger.

While the Koryŏ royalty and ministers were thus preoccupied, report after report received in Kaegyŏng told of the gradual waxing of the Sambyŏlch'o Elite Corps' strength. The area in southern Koryŏ under its dominance extended eastward from Changhŭnbu in South Chŏlla province to Happ'o and Kimju in South Kyŏngsang province; and corpsmen occupied more than thirty coastal islands.

Colonial Administrator Hindu's initial task upon arriving in Kaegyŏng was to subsume all Mongol units under his personal command. Ahai, recalled to Yen-tu from the battlefront in southern Koryŏ, bequeathed his command to Hindu. Mongkut, in charge of the military occupation of northern Koryŏ, was ordered home, and his army was brought under Hindu's command. So too was Hong Tagu's one-thousand-strong army of expatriate Koreans, as well as another newly arrived army of expatriates, also one thousand strong, under the joint command of the two sons of the lord of Yŏngnyŏng Prince Chun, Hui and Ong. Prince Chun, a commander in Torenka's army, had returned home to Liaotung because of illness, and had been replaced by his two sons. The other two Mongol generals, Kurimchi and Wang Kuo-ch'ang, were relieved of their commands. Thus Hindu alone among the Mongols held supreme authority in Koryŏ, and his presence was a formidable one. From about this time the presence in Koryŏ of the twenty-eight-year-old general, Hong Tagu, began gradually to loom larger.

In his negotiations with the Mongol military, King Wŏnjong met often with Hindu and Hong Tagu. Hindu would be the speaker, Hong Tagu remaining silent for the most part. But Hindu never failed to glance at Hong Tagu when the conversation turned to crucial matters. He would glimpse the expression in Hong's eyes, then either respond agreeably or object. Hong's constant presence was nettling to the king. It was nettling to all members of the court. If one contemplated Hindu's remarks and train of thought, one could detect his effort to understand Koryŏ's position. There were no signs of a similar sympathy in Hong Tagu, whose utterances were restricted to "agreed" or "reject." Whenever he said "reject," his voice was cold and fell disagreeably on the ears of the Koryŏ courtiers.

In mid-April, Hindu left Kaegyŏng at the head of an army to

attack the elite corps units concentrated on Chin Island. Under his command were the two sons of the lord of Yŏngnyŏng Prince Chun, each leading a contingent of troops. A fortnight later, Hong Tagu left with an army made up entirely of Korean expatriates. On both occasions, King Wŏnjong stood outside the palace to bid the chastising forces farewell. Those armies were, after all, marching in order to quell a rebellion in his country. Kubilai had ordered them into battle, and formal gestures of farewell were obligatory courtesies to Kubilai.

The campaign was executed with surprising swiftness. The combined army of units commanded by Hindu, Hong Tagu, and the two sons of Prince Chun, and yet another led by Kim Pang-gyŏng, attacked Chin Island and crushed the rebel stronghold. One report of victory followed on another, and King Wŏnjong despatched a courier to Kubilai as each was received. The king learned that more than ten thousand members of the elite corps, both men and women, had been taken captive; the lord of Sŭnghwa Prince On, whom the elite corps had elevated to king, was executed, and the leader of the rebels, Pae Chungson, had been slain in battle; one Kim T'ongjŏng had gathered the remnants of the defeated corpsmen and fled to Cheju, a large island far off the south Korean coast.

As the campaign continued, the streets of Kaegyŏng once again acquired an ambience appropriate to a city that was a nation's capital. With the greater part of the Mongol army removed far to the south, Tartars were no longer conspicuous amid the throngs of Korean men and women. Markets again emerged on the city streets, and merchants raised their voices to shrieks to attract strollers. The penury of the Koreans was evident in their shabbiness. But those Koreans who lived in the capital were far better off than their countrymen in outlying farming villages whose many grievances were conveyed daily through provincial officials to the royal court.

On June 7, the king despatched Crown Prince Sim to the Mongol court to describe the success of the military operations against the elite corps, and to explain the plight brought on by the stationing of a colonial army. Sim's most crucial assignment was to convince Kubilai that his exaction of food for the colonial army had placed Koryŏ in extremely difficult circumstances.

Just around that time, a curious rumor was whispered about the streets of Kaegyŏng. Whatever its source, it said that the reports of Mongol victories were not true, that the elite corps had defeated the combined army under Hindu's command, and that both Hindu and Hong Tagu lay dead on the battleground on Chin Island. That rumor, having acquired the guise of truth, penetrated the royal palace as far as the intimate sphere of the ladies-in-waiting. On Kanghwa Island the air was said to be rife with rumors of the imminent return of the Sambyŏlch'o Elite Corps.

Despite the king's strict orders to suppress unfounded hearsay, that rumor persisted until the moment the Mongol army returned, unit following unit, marching into Kaegyŏng city at spaced intervals.

On the day of the triumphant re-entry in early July, the king proceeded to the capital's South Gate to welcome the returning army. The first to pass through the rebuilt gate, in the company of an echelon of cavalry guardsmen, was the commanding general Hindu. Following were his subordinate units, commanded by Kim Panggyŏng, Hong Tagu, and the sons of Prince Chun. The king had not seen Kim Pang-gyŏng in some ten months. When Kim left Kaegyŏng together with Ahai in September the year before, he was determined to meet with staff officers of the elite corps to persuade them of their folly. He would risk death in accomplishing this, but the opportunity had eluded him. Kim Pang-gyŏng, the only Korean general to have held a command position in the war against the elite corps of Koryŏ, must have been troubled by an inner turmoil of conflicting emotions. During his brief absence, his country had veered onto a path more precipitous than before. Only when he passed directly before the king did he turn his head and reveal a face burned a deep mahogany by the pitiless summer sun. Although he had left the capital with fewer than seventy men under his command, the unit that followed him numbered approximately one thousand; it included, in addition to men conscripted in the provinces, elite corps soldiers who had switched their allegiance to enter his command.

CHAPTER 5

THE MONGOL ambassador Chao Liang-pi left Kaegyŏng in mid-August of 1271, the twelfth year of King Wŏnjong's reign. Joining him was Sŏ Ch'o, Korean mediator with the rank of commander, appointed by the king to conduct the ambassador to Japan. The mission, the fifth of its kind to leave from Koryŏ, consisted of more than one hundred men. It was the first to leave from Kaegyŏng, the previous four having left from Kangdo. King Wŏnjong bade his courtiers accompany the Mongol mission to the bank of the Han River, just south of the Hanyang Mountain Fortress (present-day Seoul). A report received one month later from Happ'o said that the Mongol mission had set sail on September 6. It was sent by General Kurimchi, who had preceded the ambassador to Happ'o with his army of occupation. Wŏnjong promptly despatched a courier to report this information to the Mongol court.

The excitement surrounding the Mongol mission's departure having subsided, King Wŏnjong found the leisure to compose a petition addressed to the imperial secretariat in Yen-tu, protesting the extreme difficulty of providing logistical support for the Mongol military colonies. Although Crown Prince Sim was in Yen-tu to plead Koryŏ's case, conditions were now far worse than what Sim had been prepared to describe. Koryŏ was under orders to supply all of the food and animal feed needed by the Mongols through autumn, and the end of autumn was near. But the colonial administration in Pongju had abruptly extended the obligatory period to September of the following year. Koryŏ could not survive such an exaction.

King Wŏnjong himself composed the text of the petition, consulting closely with Kim Pang-gyŏng. Having spent much time in southern Koryŏ during the campaign against the elite corps, Kim was acquainted with the living conditions of the farmers and was well advised of their woes and complaints. The text of the petition was composed in a style that reflected Kim's character: it came directly to the point, with none of the usual epistolary embellishments:

Allow me to say, on the basis of an undistorted view of my nation's past, that over the years we have possessed only a meager accumulation of grains. Your troops and steeds have been in my country since the past year. In the beginning, my courtiers and officials supplied your army with provisions, but the amount we could supply was insufficient. Subsequently, on four or five occasions, I exacted additional foodstuffs from our civil and military officials and from every farming household. The quantity of fodder for army horses, to be supplied through the season of autumn, amounts to more than one hundred fifty thousand piculs in Chinese measure. We have endured hardship in order to raise the amounts required by your army, but we are unable to continue to supply the requested quantity. Kim Pang-gyŏng, general of the chastising army, has reported, "All our farmers are subsisting on grass, nuts, and leaves. Though I would summon them for questioning, none had the strength to bring himself into my presence." The Mongol army in Koryŏ maintains three horses for each of its six thousand soldiers, eighteen thousand horses in all. Each horse requires five *sung* of feed daily. The quantity of fodder required between this October and February of next year will amount to one hundred thirty-five thousand piculs, or two hundred seventy thousand piculs in Korean measure. In addition, each of the four thousand draft animals requires five *sung* of feed daily. Between this October and March of next year, the farm oxen will require thirty-six thousand Chinese piculs of feed, or seventy-two thousand in Korean measure. The starvation of my small nation's farmers notwithstanding, the supply of food available for your imperial troops will surely fall short of the amount required. By being truthful, I risk censure for not having devised appropriate measures. Yet, I must say that if our plight should be prolonged and we attempt to endure what cannot be endured, the consequence would be irreversible tragedy. I implore you to favor us with compassion and allow those of our people who survive, enfeebled though they may be, to continue to inspire the air that renders them vital.

Kim Pang-gyŏng had assumed sole responsibility for negotiating with the colonial administration on Koryŏ's behalf, and his duties took him back and forth frequently between Kaegyŏng and Pongju. Others who had attempted the task had been frustrated by the Mongol administrator's tendency to dispense admonition without allowing them to express their wishes. Kim became an exception. He was held in high esteem among the Mongol officers of the colonial administration because he had commanded an army in the recent campaign and he knew and worked closely with Hindu and Hong Tagu. His irreproachable character also earned him their respect. His unpretentious, ingenuous nature was consonant with the image he projected—not unlike that of a wizened tiller of the soil. He formulated his opinions deliberately, and voiced them with frankness. The Mongol officers recognized his total absorption in efforts to help his country and people; they could detect not a glimmer of self-interest. They deferred to him on most matters. Thanks to that prestige and to his persistence, Kim was able to resolve the most vexing of the problems now facing Koryŏ.

Pongju, headquarters of the colonial administration, lay on the southern fringe of the territories of the northern border and western seas, far from Kaegyŏng. A great many laborers were needed to haul vast quantities of provisions over the long distances to Pongju. Koryŏ's financial burden would be reduced if the distances of the hauls could be shortened.

Kim Pang-gyŏng took this matter up with Hindu, who acknowledged the legitimacy of the grievance and recommended to Kubilai that the headquarters be relocated nearer to Koryŏ's capital. The grievance had been entered in September of the previous year, and Kubilai's approval had been issued in late January. But if the colonial administration was to be relocated, so too must the colonial army. Billets and stables would have to be built at the new location. Selecting a new site was no easy matter. Hindu himself braved the harsh winter weather to inspect a number of potential sites. Some he visited several times before finally selecting two, Yŏmju and Paekchu, as the new dual headquarters.

When Kim Pang-gyŏng was informed of Kubilai's favorable decision, he hastened to Pongju and thanked Hindu for his kindness. "I have been touched to the core by your great kindness," Kim said, "so much so that I wish to offer you my life as a gesture of gratitude."

"It was not I," Hindu replied, "but His Imperial Majesty who responded to your grievance. I merely carried out his command."

Hong Tagu chanced to be present. "A rare offer, indeed . . . Let me, then, be the one to hold your life in custody." He spoke as if he quite meant to extract Kim's life from his body for safekeeping elsewhere. Hindu chuckled, but neither Kim nor Hong Tagu shared his merriment. The aged general, on whose thin shoulders Koryŏ's fate rested, and the young administrator of expatriate Koreans exchanged sharp glances, their eyes locking for a brief instant before involuntarily looking away.

*

As the year 1271 was drawing to a close, King Wŏnjong was informed that Yi Chang-yong's illness had become critical. Because propriety forbade his visiting Yi, who had been banished from court in the previous year, the king sent a trusted attendant daily to inquire after him, and to take him medicines. Although many thought that Yi would not survive the year, his condition became stable and he lived to see the coming of the year 1272.

On January 18, the Mongol scribe Chang To, a member of Chao Liang-pi's mission, returned to Kaegyŏng together with twelve Japanese, Yashirō among them. The embassy had sailed back to Happ'o on the thirteenth, and Chang To had been sent ahead of the others to hasten back to the Mongol court with his report on the mission.

According to Chang To, the embassy had set sail from Kimju on September 6, and on the nineteenth had landed at Imazu, from which they proceeded a few miles inland to the west guard post of Dazaifu on the island of Kyushu. Because Chao Liang-pi's wish to deliver the state paper to Japan's capital was denied, he presented the governor with a duplicate, retaining the original copy, and stated his expectation of receiving an official reply no later than the month of November. Receiving no reply, he had returned, bringing

Yashirō and eleven other Japanese with him. Those twelve Japanese were not, of course, envoys of Japan, much less bearers of a nonexistent reply. Very likely many Japanese functionaries of that locality were inclined to accept an offer of travel to China, for they knew that two others before them, who had gone to the land of the Mongols at the behest of visiting envoys, had been entertained in splendid fashion and then brought back safely.

It went without saying that this ambassador, Chao Liang-pi, like those who had preceded him to Japan, had failed in his mission. King Wŏnjong reflected gloomily on Kubilai's perception of that failure. Kubilai had pacified four-fifths of what had once been the great Sung Empire and, on November 15 of the previous year, had instituted the dynastic title of Yuan, thereby establishing the Yuan Empire of China, the Middle Kingdom of the world. Yet every embassy he sent to Japan had been treated with indignity. The Japanese refused to accept the papers they carried, much less honor them with replies. Kubilai's alternatives had been reduced to exercising the phrase "resort to the force of arms," which he had included in his message for its menacing effect.

King Wŏnjong had accepted Yi Chang-yong's counsel and had secretly despatched his own envoy to Japan two months prior to Chao Liang-pi's departure. He had schemed to alert the Japanese to the imminent arrival of Chao's mission and to its purpose. He knew that the instrument entrusted to his own envoy had been accepted by the Dazaifu officials and transmitted to the Bakufu, the shogun's central headquarters in Kamakura. He had believed that the effect of his letter would be revealed in some subtle way in the Bakufu's reception of the ambassador of the Yuan Empire. His expectations betrayed, Wŏnjong felt driven to extreme vexation by the senseless arrogance of that tiny nation which lay beyond the insulating barrier of wind and waves. He cared little if Japan were laid waste by Mongol soldiers. But he could not endure seeing Koryŏ destroyed through involvement in a war between the Mongols and the Japanese. Koryŏ's courtiers, soldiers, and farmers already felt the ache of hunger. When he imagined an army of conquest setting sail aboard warships from Happ'o, he also saw the great majority of his countrymen dead from starvation, Koryŏ's vast forests denuded of trees.

The nation with the illustrious name of Koryŏ would by then have ceased to exist.

Before the sun had set on the day of Chang To's return, King Wŏnjong sent a message describing the outcome of the Mongol mission to Yi Chang-yong, who lay languishing in his sickbed. Yi replied quickly, and the king eagerly read what he had written:

> Your enriching influence, ever spreading, has extended as far as the region where the sun originates, and all nations have yielded to the delights of the harmony that pervades the realm beneath Heaven. The Japanese are the only people isolated by the sea. Your surrogate Chao Liang-pi came to Kimju this past September, boarded a ship, and sailed off into the great sea. On the thirteenth day of January, he arrived back in Happ'o together with twelve officials of Japan. Truly, his success was due to the benign tranquility imparted by saintly virtues on high. The Japanese have come in order to feel the bracing Imperial winds, wishing to yield to them. Abruptly they crossed the waters, coming at last to make proper obeisance. The myriad countries now gaze up to Heaven. How could my heart not but rejoice? I hasten to despatch my humble envoy to bring felicitations to the imperial preserve.

This was all that Yi Chang-yong had written. Clearly it was the text of a memorial, composed in recognition of the need to provide Kubilai with such. Yi provided no explanation, but King Wŏnjong could read the mind of the aged minister, who lay at the threshold of death. Although he had spent many long years together with Yi, never before had he perceived Yi's thoughts so clearly. It seemed as if he could hear Yi whispering close beside him: ". . . If this text is appropriate, I ask that it be sent. If it is not, I ask that it be destroyed. Having been absent from court for an entire year, I know nothing of the delicate issues that now affect our country's diplomacy. I merely indited what entered my mind at the moment. Suffering extreme debility and hovering not far from death, I am unable to devise counsel that may be of greater value."

King Wŏnjong promptly had a fair copy made of Yi's draft. It would be a congratulatory memorial addressed to Kubilai and predicated on a tacit agreement among all persons concerned—that

Yashirō and his eleven countrymen were emissaries sent by Japan. The king did not care what the consequences might be—Koryŏ had no alternative. Kubilai might well accept this statement born of an effort that had surely drained Yi Chang-yong of precious vitality; he might very well acquiesce. If his anger toward Japan should subside for a period of time, Koryŏ would be the beneficiary. The arrival of that moment which was Koryŏ's greatest dread had to be delayed. The king would grasp at any opportunity for a delay, however brief, of even a day. For who could say that Kubilai, during that one day, might not chance upon a reason to shift his angry gaze, now fixed upon Japan, to another part of the world?

King Wŏnjong consulted Chang To regarding the advisability of presenting such a memorial to Kubilai. Chang To replied that the ambassador, Chao Liang-pi, and all who had accompanied him would indeed be grateful if the outcome of the mission were to be so described. Chang To remained less than a day in Kaegyŏng, departing quickly for Yen-tu together with the twelve Japanese. Also in his company was Paek Kŏ, whom the king had appointed translator with the rank of commander. Paek Kŏ would present the memorial to Kubilai.

On January 28, a scant ten days after that day of flurry, Yi Chang-yong was dead. He was seventy-two, and childless. He had provided for his own cremation, and his body was consigned to the flames by three monks. Although the cold that day was biting, the winds did not stir and the smoke from the funeral pyre rose straight into the sky.

*

Crown Prince Sim returned from the Mongol Empire on February 10. He had left eight months earlier to meet with Kubilai and plead Koryŏ's difficulty in supplying the Mongol colonial army with provisions. He had returned in early autumn, then left again in December as he had in previous years to participate in the New Year's festivities at Kubilai's court. Since the Im Yŏn affair he had traveled more frequently between Kaegyŏng and Yen-tu as a bearer of petitions. When he returned this time, he and every member of his retinue of more than thirty men were clad in Tartar apparel and had their heads partly shaved and the remaining hair plaited in Mongol fashion.

Upon seeing the crown prince, who had hastened to the royal palace, Wŏnjong rebuked him for forsaking the cherished customs of his native country. "How could it be a hardship," his son retorted, "for men of Koryŏ attending the Mongol court to conform to their customs if that conformity serves to reduce the burden they have imposed on Koryŏ?" Wŏnjong had no ready rejoinder to his son's reply. True, changing one's appearance by adopting Mongol dress mattered little if it would alleviate his people's suffering. But he averted his gaze from his son, who stood before him in an alien guise.

Sim continued on, emboldened by his father's meekness. "Mongolia is no longer the land of the Mongols of times past. It has become the great Yuan Empire. That empire is far more powerful and possesses far greater wealth and military might than anything you, my royal father, can imagine. Envoys from other nations gather at Kubilai's court for the New Year's ceremony in numbers you would not believe, and the splendor of the ceremonial proceedings defies description in words. I alone among Koreans can accurately assess Koryŏ's standing as a nation. Koryŏ at present maintains the dignity of an independent nation, but this belies our actual status as a tributary state of the Yuan Empire. We cannot so much as repair our palace gates without Kubilai's express approval. Having visited the Mongol capital often, I have come to know Kubilai's sentiments and the attitude of those in the Bureau of Military Affairs and the Yuan Imperial Secretariat. They do not, as you do, regard Koryŏ as an independent nation. You must put aside your vision of the past. Acknowledge Kubilai as suzerain, and consider yourself to be the head of one of his subject states. Only then may you find a way to preserve our nation. I doubt that Koryŏ can otherwise survive.

"You once accepted Yi Chang-yong's counsel and entered a request to Kubilai, seeking the hand of his daughter on my behalf. Even though that request was rejected, I believe that Yi was right. A small country is hard pressed to maintain its nationhood when a great empire lies just beyond its border, but difficulties vanish when the smaller nation chooses to become part of its greater neighbor. Koryŏ must have appeared comical, seeking the hand of an imperial princess at the time it did. Kubilai could not have consented, not knowing whether tiny Koryŏ, long a militant adversary, would be his friend or foe. But times have changed. Every year at the New Year's festivity, my seating has advanced steadily toward that of highest honor. This year, Kubilai himself personally designated my placement."

Sim's fervor bespoke his pride in having rendered his country the great service of working himself gradually into Kubilai's confidence. He might after all be correct in his presumption, Wŏnjong mused. Sim was blessed with an ingrained sense of propriety. Now thirty-seven, he displayed a new maturity of character and astuteness. He would fare well in a comparison with any crown prince of any nation. As Sim had said, Koryŏ might chance upon a way to survive as a nation if it subordinated itself fully to Kubilai. But there was also the possibility that Koryŏ would thereby forfeit her existence as a nation. Yi Chang-yong's plan to seek an alliance through marriage was an expedient, nothing more. Sim apparently had a different purpose in mind—or so it seemed to his father.

"You may wear Mongol dress and style your hair as they do, but only when you present yourself at the Yuan court," Wŏnjong said. "When at home, conform to our ways." He rose abruptly and left the room.

Following closely on Crown Prince Sim's return from the north, Chao Liang-pi brought his party from southern Koryŏ to the capital. Fully aware of his responsibility for his mission's failure, Chao decided to stay in Kaegyŏng and there await further orders from Kubilai.

In March, King Wŏnjong sent an emissary to Cheju Island to summon the elite corps leaders to a council. Selected as emissary was Kŭm Hun, deputy chamberlain of the Office of the Royal Archives. Because the Sambyŏlch'o Elite Corps had been dealt a crippling blow at Chin Island the year before, the king thought their leaders might acknowledge his summons. He did not wish to prolong the bloodshedding among Koreans; the conflict would have to be resolved to forestall yet another incursion of Mongol troops.

Of the more than thirty men in the royal mission, only Kǔm Hun returned. The party had been captured by elite corpsmen as it navigated the waters between Chin and Cheju islands, and all were being held captive except for Kǔm Hun, who had been cast adrift in a small boat. He returned with the royal summons, which the corps leader Kim T'ongjǒng had refused to accept.

According to Kǔm Hun, the members of the elite corps were not inclined to capitulate. They prided themselves in their self-appointed role as the only defenders of the nation, and they boasted that they would soon expel the Mongols from Koryǒ and liberate their starving countrymen.

Again there were reports from the southern coastal area of renewed belligerence by the elite corps. Having constructed inner and outer fortifications on Cheju Island, the elite corps brazenly roamed the seas, plundering one coastal town after another and capturing ships, storehouses of grain, and human booty. As it gained strength, the elite corps gradually, but unmistakably, began to reveal its true nature. As all such bands inevitably must, so had the elite corps begun its descent into piracy.

Deprived of further means of redemption, King Wǒnjong despatched Kǔm Hun to the Yuan court to describe the current state of affairs, and General Na Yu to quell the elite corps bands that harassed Chǒlla province. But the insurgents were elusive and could not be engaged in battles that could produce claims of victory.

Although Kim Pang-gyǒng wished to lead the troops into battle, he remained indispensable as the only effective intermediary between the Mongol colonial administration and the overburdened people of the eleven colonial districts.

On April 3, Chang To returned from Yen-tu. He brought back the twelve Japanese he had taken with him. Kubilai had refused to grant the Japanese an audience, knowing that they were mere functionaries from Dazaifu. He further suspected them to be scouts sent by the wary Japanese to assess the strength of the Yuan Empire. The imperial secretariat in Yen-tu shared this suspicion.

Chang To had been ordered by the secretariat to take the twelve Japanese home. He left Kaegyǒng on April 7 to resume his journey to Japan. King Wǒnjong ordered the censor Kang Chiso to accom-

pany the travelers. Several days later, Chao Liang-pi left Kaegyŏng
on his second attempt to fulfill his mission as ambassador to Japan.
Again the king had a contingent of his vassals escort the party as far
as the Han River. The memorial that Yi Chang-yong had composed
on his deathbed had not, after all, influenced Kubilai.

This year again, the spring sped by amid such fluster that the brief
but brilliant blossoming of the golden forsythia went largely unnoticed. On April 30, Wŏnjong despatched an emissary to Yen-tu to
deliver a plea for a reduction in the amount of food requisitioned by
the colonial army.

Chang To returned from Japan in May and reported that Chao
Liang-pi, intent on honoring the imperial command, was determined to stay in Japan until the Mongol state paper was accepted by
the court of the Japanese king. That tiny island nation lying beyond
the stormy strait was an enigma to King Wŏnjong. He had been told
that pine-covered hills rose steeply from the rocky shores, against
which the sea waves beat insistently, and that the rattle of warriors'
swords and spears shattered the gentler sound of the sea winds passing through those forests of pines. But he needed more than this
brief description to imagine that country known as Japan. He contemplated a scene with the twelve Japanese visitors set against those
shores, but it lent no reality to his vision. Try though he might to
visualize Japan, he only heard the sound of waves breaking on precipitous shores.

In August, King Wŏnjong received sternly worded orders from
Kubilai: "Work closely with Hong Tagu and sweep the land clear of
the Sambyŏlch'o Elite Corps." The king solicited Kim Pang-gyŏng's
opinion before approaching Hong Tagu. An attempt must first be
made, Kim said, to regain their allegiance through royal persuasion.
Failing that, the insurgents must be subjugated by Korean forces.
The elite corps knows it is degenerating into brigandry and would
probably surrender if it believed that it might be defeated. If an
army of Mongols were sent against them, they would resist to the
last man, knowing well that surrender would mean death. Mongol
troops must not take part in the pacification. Our own army has
grown larger in the two years since the royal court returned to
Kaegyŏng, and it can suppress the insurrection without assistance

from the Mongols. When King Wŏnjong conferred with Hong
Tagu, he insisted on following the course of action Kim Pang-gyŏng
had recommended.

Hong Tagu, on his own, had learned that Kim T'ongjŏng, the
leader of the elite corps, had many kin living in Kaegyŏng. He
selected five of them to sail to Cheju Island as royal emissaries. He
then left for the southern provinces to inspect the shipbuilding
which Kubilai had enjoined upon Koryŏ. The leader of the elite
corps rejected the royal summons even though his own kin had delivered it.

From late summer through autumn, the elite corps cast off all
restraint. The theft of Chŏlla province's tax rice, an assault on the
shipbuilding facilities on Koran Island, the firing of military vessels
moored at Happ'o and Kŏje Island—these and other outrages were
perpetrated in quick succession. The attack on Koran Island was
especially vicious: over a span of several days, all the warships were
burned, the shipwrights were abducted, and every official and
laborer at the shipyard was put to the sword. This might have been
considered one of many acts representing a wholesale rejection of
Yuan Empire policies toward Koryŏ. But raids on poorly guarded
districts with intent only to abduct and pillage were acts of piracy.
The raiders had begun to group themselves in fleets that often
moored at Yŏnghŭng Island, menacing the entire Kyonggi province
coast.

As the year was drawing to a close, Hong Tagu returned briefly to
Kaegyŏng, then left for Yen-tu. When he again returned in March,
he met with King Wŏnjong and communicated Kubilai's order to
take Cheju Island. Operational orders were issued the next day.
Hindu and Hong Tagu were to lead an army of Mongols, and Kim
Pang-gyŏng was appointed commander of the army of Koryŏ. More
than two hundred warships that had been built in the coastal provinces were diverted to the southern sea. The combined chastising
force was to consist of two thousand Mongols, two thousand Chinese, and six thousand Koreans. To organize such a large army of
Korean troops, all guard units, which had been scattered widely
among the provincial districts, needed to be recalled.

The campaign against Cheju Island had been planned on such a grand scale that both King Wŏnjong and Kim Pang-gyŏng perceived a purpose beyond the mere pacification of the elite corps. Evidently it was a preparatory exercise for the organization at some later date of an expeditionary force to conquer Japan. Both the king and Kim Pang-gyŏng protested the seeming impossibility of mobilizing six thousand Korean soldiers, but Hong Tagu would not be moved. His reply was simple: "Kubilai has so ordered it." And Kim was compelled to search for new recruits to add to the ranks of his army.

On the eve of his departure at the head of six thousand Korean troops gathered from all parts of Koryŏ, Kim Pang-gyŏng said to his king, "I do not doubt that the elite corpsmen on Cheju will be slaughtered. I too am determined to show them no mercy. I hope that I may be forgiven if I succeed in this task."

"You have made the correct decision," Wŏnjong replied.

Not long after the campaigning armies left for the Naju coast, Kaegyŏng welcomed the return of Chao Liang-pi's mission, which had been in Japan for a year. Chao appeared haggard in the extreme. He had been held in Dazaifu during his entire stay, forbidden to travel to the capital. Again he had returned, his mission unfulfilled.

King Wŏnjong feted Chao Liang-pi in recognition of his sacrificial endeavor, and during the banquet presented him with three *kun* of silver and ten bolts of ramie cloth. The *darughachi* Li I also offered him gifts, but Chao refused them, saying, "Those items were appropriated from the people of Koryŏ, and I cannot accept them." Having traveled the full length of Koryŏ and many times more between Kaegyŏng and Happ'o, he knew well the unspeakable misery of the people, and may have felt compelled thus to express his sympathy.

"Japan seems to expect an invasion by the Mongols," Chao said. "Such were the rumors circulating through Dazaifu. The seacoast appeared to be well fortified. With Japan assuming such a belligerent stance, I believe that an army of conquest will surely be sent overseas. You should consider it inevitable."

For but an instant the king felt Chao's sharp gaze directed at him. "Did he learn about the envoy I sent to Japan?" he wondered. Perhaps Chao Liang-pi knew everything and was now giving him counsel, warning him of the extraordinary perseverance that would soon be required of Koryŏ. The king felt a fondness for this Mongol emissary. Chao Liang-pi differed from the others who had come from the land of the Mongols. During his sojourn of several months when he had first come to Kaegyŏng as the Mongol ambassador bound for Japan, he had refrained from interfering in Koryŏ's domestic affairs. He behaved as though he recognized the bounds of his duties and was disinclined to overstep them. Upon returning from his first mission, he sent Chang To to report to Kubilai, himself remaining in Kaegyŏng until his second departure for Japan. His refusal to seek an opportunity for self-justification inspired Wŏn-jong's admiration.

Approximately one month after Chao left for Yen-tu, news of a great victory was received from the chastising army. The combined land and sea forces of ten thousand men had set sail from Pŏnnam district in Naju and, after landing at three separate points on Cheju Island, had surrounded Cheju Fortress, headquarters of the elite corps. When their stronghold fell, Kim T'ongjŏng killed himself and the thirteen hundred men under his command vacated the fortress and surrendered. The insurgence of the Sambyŏlch'o Elite Corps of Kangdo, which had defied royal authority for three years, was put down with finality in April of 1273.

In May, units of the triumphant army returned to Kaegyŏng at measured intervals. The last of them, under Kim Pang-gyŏng's command, returned in June. Kim informed King Wŏnjong of an ominous indication: the Yuan Empire appeared to be taking Cheju Island under its jurisdiction. An army of five hundred Mongols and two hundred Koreans had been left on Cheju, this ratio of Mongols to Koreans having been determined by Hong Tagu. As Kim saw it, Koryŏ troops should have occupied Cheju, and there was no reason for more than twice their number of Mongol troops to be left on the island. But indebted as he was for the support the Yuan army had given him, Kim could not override the Mongol commanders' insistence.

The sureness of Kim's prediction was soon borne out. Two months later, two Mongol officers passed through Kaegyŏng en route to Cheju. One, named Shih Li-po, held the title of Commissioner for the Pacification of the Cheju Nation; the other, named I Pang-pao, was his deputy. The assignment of a commissioner meant that Cheju Island was being placed under Yuan jurisdiction, just as the northwest sector of Koryŏ had when Ch'oe T'an ceded it to the Mongols.

That was but one small eddy in the dizzying tide of events that began to swirl about King Wŏnjong following the Cheju campaign. In June Colonial Administrator Hindu was recalled from Koryŏ, and in the following month, Kim Pang-gyŏng was abruptly summoned to the Yuan capital. Mongol military and civil officials traveled back and forth between the two countries with greater frequency. Several men with the title of shipbuilding supervisor came into Kaegyŏng. Daily the king was subjected to the thrumming of Mongols pressing for military provisions, and of his own people pleading for a reprieve.

For once, however, the Korean king received tidings that provided momentary solace: upon returning to Yen-tu, Chao Liang-pi had been summoned into Kubilai's presence and commended with the words, "You did not disgrace the imperial commission." Rejoicing on behalf of the only Yuan official whose friendship for Koryŏ he did not doubt, the king felt as if he had glimpsed a small patch of blue in a perennially grey overcast.

As the season advanced from summer to autumn, a courier brought tidings from Kim Pang-gyŏng, who had left for Yen-tu in July. When Kim had presented himself at the imperial palace, he had been seated next to the prime minister to partake of food and drink. No one at that banquet was accorded greater honors than Kim, on whom Kubilai bestowed a gold-lacquered saddle, a robe of silk brocade, and generous amounts of gold and silver. Kim, at the time, regarded those gifts as rewards not for his recent valor, but for a great responsibility yet to be borne. The description in his letter of what he could grasp of trends of thought prevalent in the Yuan capital suggested that the coming autumn might be the time when all of Koryŏ, sovereign and subjects alike, would have to confront a national emergency of unprecedented magnitude.

In October, Hong Tagu was again summoned back to Yen-tu. Before leaving Kaegyŏng, he specified the amount of foodstuffs to be accumulated during the current year and the number of laborers to be conscripted to log and transport timber from the forested regions. Both demands far exceeded what Koryŏ could supply.

In November, a newly arrived Yuan envoy elaborated on the earlier tidings concerning Chao Liang-pi. When Chao was asked by Kubilai whether or not to subjugate Japan, he gave this answer. "During my year's stay in Japan, I observed her people and customs closely. The Japanese are fond of wanton killing. They are ignorant of propriety in the relationship between parents and children. Their land, mostly mountains and streams, is unfit for the cultivation of mulberry. Though we might rule Japan's people, they will not perform useful labor. Though we might possess their land, it will not add to our riches. Should we attempt a crossing to that country, our navigators will encounter irregular seasonal winds and unexpected disasters. We would, in effect, waste men and effort in an attempt to fill a bottomless chasm. Allow me to say, 'Attack them not.' "

King Wŏnjong knew that Chao Liang-pi honestly wished to spare Koryŏ an ill-deserved fate. "Attack them not! Attack them not! Attack them not!" He shouted Chao's final words of counsel over and over, as if to discern the extent to which they might have penetrated Kubilai's mind. And as he did so, those words gradually acquired the resonance of an incantation—a prayer perhaps, or a magical formula. Suddenly he noticed his own muteness; though he might shout "Attack them not!" the words failed to form an utterance. Alarmed, he shouted those words again and again, but there was only silence. He realized that his throat had assumed the inexplicable function of suppressing utterance. Courtiers who attended him closely had noticed the muteness that occasionally silenced their king. Wŏnjong had just become aware of his affliction.

In December, more than a dozen Yuan officials came to Kaegyŏng to take inventory of the stock of military food supplies in the provinces. The government of Koryŏ sent its own officials with those from the Yuan Empire to verify the amounts that had been accumulated in each of the provinces. After a hailstorm at the beginning of December, snow fell steadily, and by the end of the year a white mantle had formed over all of northern Koryŏ.

CHAPTER 6

IT SNOWED continually through the month of December, but when the new year, 1274, dawned, the sky above Koryŏ was cloudless, and the sun shed its bright rays on snow-covered mountains and fields.

The main thoroughfare and lesser avenues of Kaegyŏng were thronged with strollers, many of them clustered at shops fronting on deep snow, their keepers' entreating shouts belying the bareness of their shelves. Although the people were said to be hungry, the women and children were so gaily bedecked as to make one wonder how their families had managed to retain such finery. Fused streams of laughter and convivial shouts and shrieks followed moving crowds of strollers, whose expressions of cheer at times seemed forced, quite as if they sought to recover in the course of that one day all the joyous moments that had eluded them during the past year. The muddiness of the great thoroughfare did not discourage the residents of the capital, or the Mongol, Chinese, and Korean soldiers, most of whom tended to stroll in a group of their own like, but at times drifted convivially into groups of others. It was a New Year's scene such as no one could have envisioned eight years earlier, when Kaegyŏng had just been reestablished as Koryŏ's capital.

King Wŏnjong that day held only the briefest of New Year's ceremonies to accept formal felicitations from his courtiers and military and civil officials of the Yuan Empire.

The city appeared equally festive the next day. Multitudes moved in streams, somewhat slowly this day, along streets that were more deeply mired. Such was the sight that greeted Kim Pang-gyŏng and his men on their return to Kaegyŏng.

Kim reported directly to the palace, apologized to King Wŏnjong

112

for having failed to attend court on New Year's day, and then conveyed Kubilai's orders: three hundred great ships to be built at Chŏlla and Cheju before the end of May. He begged the king's forgiveness for bringing back the very orders whose issuance he should have prevented. "For my failure I deserve death," he said, "but I would not be able to die. My soul would refuse to leave my body until I have seen my country survive the extraordinary peril to come."

The king assured Kim Pang-gyŏng that, however startling any news he might receive, he had become so hardened as to be immune to surprise, and that he, like Kim, was determined to live through Koryŏ's coming time of great trial.

Orders for the conquest of Japan were to be transmitted to field commanders in March, Kim informed his king. The expedition would set sail in early summer. Koryŏ would have to provide a great many soldiers and laborers, and Hong Tagu would soon bring Kubilai's orders for their mobilization.

Hong Tagu arrived in Kaegyŏng on the morning of the sixth and, as Kim had done, proceeded directly to the palace for an audience with King Wŏnjong.

The decree that Hong delivered had been issued by the imperial secretariat. It stated that Koryŏ would supply all personnel and material required for the construction of three hundred great ships; that Koryŏ's subjects Hŏ Kong and Hong Nokchu were appointed commander of guard headquarters of Chŏlla and Naju provinces, respectively, to oversee the construction; and that they should report directly to Kim Pang-gyŏng, who was appointed to serve concurrently as territorial commander of the southwestern provinces and supervisor of naval construction. Hong Tagu had also been appointed supervisor of naval construction, a post he was to share coequally with Kim Pang-gyŏng while continuing to serve as the senior military and civil administrator of expatriate Koreans.

"Na Yu and other Koryŏ generals shall each assume district military commands in the five provinces of Chŏlla, Kyŏngsang, Tonggye, Sŏhae, and Kyoju," Hong said. Then he concluded, "You must levy thirty thousand five hundred shipwrights and laborers by January 15."

The many courtiers present were appalled at the outrageousness of the demand. Even Kim Pang-gyŏng, who had warned the king of extraordinary demands to come, was stunned. "Thirty thousand five hundred!" he gasped, but said no more. Hong Tagu had brought King Wŏnjong ill-omened tidings before, but never had the tidings been so sinister.

No one protested. Indeed, protesting would have been futile, for Hong Tagu had given orders he attributed to Kubilai. Only by petitioning Kubilai or the imperial secretariat could they seek redress. Furthermore, if they had told Hong Tagu that such a large number of workers could not possibly be conscripted, Hong would have prescribed ways to make it possible.

Both Mount Pyŏn in Chŏnju province and Mount Ch'ongwan in Naju province, shipbuilding sites designated by the secretariat, were heavily forested and close to the sea. The fact that such ideal sites had been selected suggested that Hong Tagu, who knew Koryŏ well, had designed the plan, and it had been translated into an imperial command for Kubilai to issue.

Starting that day, all Koreans, from the king and his courtiers on down to commoners throughout the land, knew the fury of a forcible levy that was to raise more than thirty thousand men in a matter of nine days. It is written in the *History of Koryŏ:* "At that time, horses formed continuous lines from one post station to the next; the manifold tasks were harrying, and the prescribed time, so brief, passed within the span of a lightning's flash, and so the people suffered." Clearly words could not adequately describe those terrible days.

Construction of the ships was to begin on January 15. Three hundred large warships had to be built by the end of May. When Kim Pang-gyŏng assumed his duties as supervisor, he was promptly confounded by the instruction specifying ships of European design, which the Mongols fancied. Such exotic ships could not possibly be built within the time that had been allowed. Kim quickly sent a courier to the secretariat requesting permission to build ships of traditional Korean design.

There were other nagging problems. Although Hong Tagu yielded to the knowledgeable Kim Pang-gyŏng insofar as the design of the ships was concerned, he refused to heed any other suggestion or plea. He simply stood fast, prodding the Koreans to work faster. The orders that the king and Kim dreaded most were yet to come. In addition to soldiers, Koryŏ would surely be expected to provide a maritime labor force. The population had been decimated by the recent conscription of shipbuilding workers. If the few remaining men were called into military service, there would be no one left to serve as seamen and laborers. Koryŏ's people had already been reduced to desperation by the injunction to feed the Mongol colonial army. A greater exaction would mean that not even a grain of rice could be kept for their own consumption.

The king needed to inform the Mongols of Koryŏ's plight. He thought that a candid description of his nation's plight would elicit sympathy. If "even Heaven is touched by sincere supplications," as a well-known proverb had it, would not Kubilai, who possessed a human heart, be moved?

King Wŏnjong took up his writing brush. Dispensing with the conventions of formal epistolary prose, he composed sentences that contained not one decorative word or phrase that might dilute the substance of his message:

> The edict from the Secretariat, delivered to me on January 2 by my subject the vice minister Kim Pang-gyŏng, enjoined us to construct three hundred great ships at Chŏlla and Cheju. In accordance with instructions conveyed to me on January 6 by Hong Tagu, I ordered my subjects Hŏ Kong and Hong Nokchu to recruit the specified number of artisans and laborers and gather an adequate supply of lumber and other materials, and then despatched Kim Pang-gyŏng to supervise the construction. The assignment being substantial and my nation being weak, I fear lest our accomplishments fall short of sufficiency. In our modest nation, we in the the past did not make a distinction between soldier and farmer. If we conscript our people for corvée over many months or seasons, who will tend to the farms? Such questions aside, however, we are determined to perform this task.
>
> Construction of the ships was begun on January 15. A total of 30,500 craftsmen and laborers are at work. If each worker is to be given three meals daily over a period of three months, we shall need

34,312 piculs of rice. The Imperial Secretariat on January 19 informed us that Hindu's territorial army of 1,500 men will take up station in Kimju, and has instructed us to fill its need for 1,570 piculs of rice during the period of occupation. Additionally, we must provide rice for the detachment of 500 men assigned to Supervisor of Naval Construction Hong Tagu. Already we have delivered seven months' food supply, totaling 2,904 piculs, for the 1,400 men of the occupying army at Cheju. My modest nation has also supplied 8,000 piculs of food and 1,325 piculs of fodder to the troops commanded by Ouro and Kutechi in Naju. Furthermore, in accordance with directives received from the Imperial Secretariat, we have been supplying all 10,223 farmers of Cheju with animal feed since December of 1273. The present scarcity of both food and fodder cannot be alleviated. Exactions made of our own civil and military personnel and of the One Hundred aristocratic families have been extreme.

Last year we built war vessels for the use of your great army, which sailed to Cheju Island in April, annihilating the rebels and departing in May. Because our farmers failed to till their fields, autumn brought virtually no harvest. The provisions we have supplied to maintain those men now at the shipyards, the great number of army horses, and the farmers of Cheju have amounted to more than 40,000 piculs. We have been exceedingly hard pressed to provide for the armies occupying Kimju, Chŏnju, and Naju. Pursuant to subsequent orders from the Secretariat, we have delivered supplemental provisions—2,047 piculs of food and 1,001 piculs of cattle feed—to the colonial army in Pongju to offset its shortages.

If I fail to inform you now of the extremely dire situation in Koryŏ, I would have great difficulty answering to charges of laggardness at a later date. Because all of us bordering on the four seas reside as members of a single house, your soldiers and steeds dwell in our land as well. The One Hundred families are all people under the wings of the One Imperial Person. I prostrate myself as I express my hope that you will feel pity and favor us with the benevolence you bestow on all others.

This petition was delivered to the Yuan Imperial Secretariat in February by Yi In, who had been commissioned acting general by King Wŏnjong.

On March 13, Hong Tagu received a communication from Colonial Administrator Hindu specifying August as the month for chastising the Japanese. Hindu ordered Koryŏ to mobilize a supporting army of 5,600 men, the same number of Korean troops he had ordered conscripted for the attack on Cheju Island. That number was once available and should be available again, he apparently thought. Then came orders for Koryŏ to mobilize a working force of 6,700 navigators, boatsmen, and other seamen to man the warships. If these numbers were to be added to the 30,500 already conscripted for shipbuilding, the result would mean the disappearance of young men from every garden and field in Koryŏ.

In early April, King Wŏnjong despatched Royal Remonstrator Kwak Yŏp'il to the Mongol Empire to deliver another plea:

> Earlier, the enfeebled populace of my modest nation was pressed into service for the war on Cheju Island, and at present many are employed to build ships. Now we must conscript soldiers and seamen to serve in a war of conquest. Through Hong Tagu and Kim Panggyŏng, you have given us orders to build three hundred warships and mobilize fifteen thousand seamen. The amounts are far beyond what my modest nation can provide. The people of Cheju Island and cities in the Tongnyŏng-pu jurisdiction are familiar with the sea and skilled at handling ships; I ask that they be chosen instead for this task.
>
> The demand for army food provisions, continuous since 1270, has depleted our supply. I have appropriated the stipends of our civil and military officials and of the one hundred aristocratic families in an attempt to raise the amount of food required by the thirty thousand five hundred men engaged in shipbuilding and by the many Yuan armies in Koryŏ and on Cheju Island. We have levied many taxes, yet we have not been able to meet your demands fully. Yuan and Koryŏ officials have expropriated everything our farmers possessed, and there is no more.
>
> I prostrate myself, imploring you to accept twenty thousand piculs as the total amount of food to be provided by my modest nation, so that all my people may rejoice and remain forever grateful for your imperial kindness.

An emissary bearing a rescript from Kubilai arrived in Kaegyŏng just as Kwak Yŏp'il left for Yen-tu. King Wŏnjong received the emissary, anticipating a reply to the petition he had submitted to the secretariat in February. Instead, he was notified that Crown Prince Sim would receive Kubilai's daughter Khutlgaimish in marriage, the nuptial ceremony to be held in Yen-tu on May 11. The king had, at Yi Chang-yong's urging, presented a request for such a betrothal, but that was four years earlier. The year after that, he was notified that Kubilai had approved the request, but had received no further word.

Prince Sim had left for the Yuan Empire in December, and Wŏnjong did not know what had led to this surprising development. He felt no excitement, and he said nothing. Indeed, he had lost his ability to produce utterance. With the loss of voice came a marked deterioration of the body. Although the royal physicians treated him daily, they could not identify the sickness.

As he lay in his sickbed, King Wŏnjong was driven to compose one letter after another to Kubilai. When he reread what he had written, he sometimes noticed that some letters repeated what he had already written or that the dating of a letter followed too closely on that of his previous letter, and these he would discard. The royal scribe withheld others for similar reasons. When Wŏnjong was preoccupied with these compositions, his eyes acquired a feverish gleam and his face was animated. He cited many kinds and instances of hardship in an attempt to make Kubilai understand that his country no longer had so much as a grain of rice to spare. He was determined to convince Kubilai that Koryŏ had dedicated itself to providing for the Mongol colonial army for so many years that his people were starving.

In May, Wŏnjong composed an unusually long plea to Kubilai. Even though he lay confined in a sickbed, he envisioned the entire land of Koryŏ in upheaval—city streets teeming with soldiers, villages populated only by women and old men whose grievous cries echoed across the heavens while they gazed upward, and reverberated through the earth as they prostrated themselves in helpless prayer. He wrote on, keeping those tragic scenes before his mind's eye. From time to time he attempted to read aloud what he had written, but his voice would not come. He had to be content with a silent reading. But the document was attached by Kim Pang-gyŏng, who thought it inappropriate to present Kubilai with such a protest during the month when his daughter would be betrothed to Crown Prince Sim.

One day an emissary from the Yuan secretariat came to Kaegyŏng to transmit Kubilai's wish for Koreans to intensify agricultural production and accumulate even greater quantities of food for the Mongol armies. Wŏnjong reached for his writing brush to write another plea, but his body would not obey his wish.

On June 16, King Wŏnjong was asked to read a letter that had been composed on his behalf. A report on the completion of the building of warships, it would be sent to the imperial secretariat following the king's approval:

> Having received imperial orders, on January 3 of this year, to build three hundred great ships, I promptly instituted measures for compliance. I despatched the assistant minister of military affairs Hŏ Kong to Mount Pyŏn in Chŏlla province, and the minister of the left Hong Nokchu to Mount Ch'ŏngwan in Naju province, to insure the production of an adequate supply of lumber. I placed the vice minister Kim Pang-gyŏng in charge of the responsible officers; they obeyed him conscientiously, and on January 15 completed their assignment of conscripting workers and gathering materials. Construction of the ships was begun on the sixteenth, and completed on the last day of May. We have built large and small vessels, nine hundred in all, and equipped them fully. Capable officials among those of the third court rank have been assigned to transport the vessels, which are now en route to Kimju. I humble myself, asking you good ministers to forward this missive to Him on high.

King Wŏnjong tried to ask why the scribe had written "large and small vessels, nine hundred in all" when three hundred was the number of ships they had been ordered to build, but his voice failed him. He traced his finger over that figure.

An official soon came to the king's bedside to explain: the total of nine hundred ships consisted of three hundred large vessels of one-thousand-picul capacity, three hundred lightweight landing crafts, and three hundred tenders to carry fresh water; the latter six hundred vessels had been built by workmen in Naju province on Hong Tagu's orders.

King Wŏnjong nodded, then closed his eyes and slipped into

meditative silence. He soon found himself visualizing the face of Hong Tagu, and the image for some reason did not inspire hatred as it had in the past. The face of the young administrator of expatriate Koreans clearly expressed his loathing of men of his own race; it was cold-hearted, but seemed neither enigmatic nor sinister. Since that morning, however, Wŏnjong had been contemplating the face of another—of Kubilai. Until the day before, he had always been able to visualize Kubilai's face and be warmed by an expression that promised sympathetic understanding of earnest pleas. But on this day, however often he tried, he could not visualize that familiar face. He saw a different face, one grown suddenly larger, that seemed to express attentiveness when in fact the man behind it was not listening at all. It was a face that would betray no emotion even though one might reach out to it with violent intent; words shouted close to its ears would fail to register. It was the face of a man who would ponder matters alone and then dictate his decisions, a man who would annex Koryŏ should he decide to, and would not hesitate to make Koryŏ a sacrificial victim of war should he decide to conquer Japan.

Wŏnjong could not comprehend why the face of Kubilai was now so strangely different. Knowing Kubilai's true nature, he should have been able to banish that face from his imagination. Yet it persisted. He wished to recall once again the warmth of Kubilai's expression when they first met, before either had ascended to the throne. If only he could do so, he thought, he might regain his peace of mind. But he could not recapture that fond vision.

Utterly spent by his imaginary confrontation with Kubilai, Wŏnjong on the following day, the seventeenth, thought only of Crown Prince Sim. He did so during brief spans of wakefulness. He would visualize his son, attired and coiffured like a Mongol, then try to expunge the vision. Perhaps, he mused, he had always disliked Mongol dress and hairstyle. He had been vaguely aware of this before, but suddenly he realized that what he had harbored was a lifelong loathing. In the next instant his consciousness was blurred.

King Wŏnjong died the following day. He was fifty-six and had reigned for fifteen years. A great many people came to the royal palace that day. That was also the day the army of conquest, fifteen thousand men garrisoned in the capital since May 14, left on its march southward to Happ'o, creating so great a stir that the tragedy within the palace attracted little notice. Crown Prince Sim still sojourned in the Yuan Empire, and Kim Pang-gyŏng had left for Happ'o at the head of an army. The courtiers met at dusk and selected emissaries who would inform Kubilai and Crown Prince Sim of the king's death. The emissaries left the capital that night. King Wŏnjong was interred the next day on a high ground south of the capital alongside earlier members of Koryŏ royalty.

Several days later, Hong Tagu and Kim Pang-gyŏng, each riding alone from separate directions, arrived in Kaegyŏng within half a day of each other. Hong Tagu visited the royal grave, then rode off to Happ'o. Kim Pang-gyŏng stayed in Kaegyŏng to sit at the helm of Koryŏ until the crown prince could return.

Hindu, supreme commander of the expeditionary forces against Japan, turned back immediately upon reaching Happ'o, sojourned in Kaegyŏng for two days, then left for Yen-tu. He undertook sudden travel not to honor the late king of Koryŏ, but to confer with Kubilai and receive final instructions on the eve of embarking for Japan.

King Wŏnjong's death was but a minor event amid the great swirl of activity created by the movements of the army of conquest, but it created an eddy sufficient to delay the launching of the expedition.

Kubilai had notified Hindu and Hong Tagu in March that the expedition would be launched in July. June went by and it was now well into the month of July, but still Kubilai sent no orders. The nine hundred war vessels built in Koryŏ languished at the port of Happ'o, and the twenty-five thousand men of the combined Yuan and Korean forces passed their days idly in settlements near the port.

On August 25, Crown Prince Sim was welcomed back to Kaegyŏng by the One Hundred court officials, who had assembled at the Mach'ŏnjŏng travel station. His official Mongol escort, Chang Huan, bearing an edict from Kubilai, preceded the crown prince's procession into the city. At the royal palace, Chang Huan read the edict, which stated that Crown Prince Sim would occupy the throne. The coronation of the new king, Ch'ungnyŏl, took place the following day.

The city of Kaegyŏng lay bathed in the soft light of the autumn sun. The Mongol units had moved to Happ'o, leaving behind only one small detachment. Most able-bodied Korean males had been pressed into service as soldiers and seamen, and only old men, women, and children were seen in the capital. The autumn winds came early that year, occasionally raising swirls of dust on the great thoroughfare. But the city appeared serene. The people talked hopefully about easier times to come in the reign of their new king, Ch'ungnyŏl.

Not long before King Ch'ungnyŏl's coronation, Kubilai had announced the appointment of Hindu as the supreme commander of the expeditionary forces, Hong Tagu as the vice commander of the right, Liu Fu-heng as the vice commander of the left, and Kim Pang-gyŏng as the territorial commander of southern Koryŏ. Appended to the above announcements were orders for the supplementary recruitment of four hundred fifty-eight Korean soldiers. Having no more men to conscript, the court officials had been unable to comply.

King Ch'ungnyŏl's first task upon assuming the throne was to find four hundred fifty-eight able-bodied men. The day after the coronation, government officials were sent out to scour the countryside for recruits. In three days' time, outcasts and slaves equal to the number specified were apprehended and herded away by Mongol guards.

On September 12, King Ch'ungnyŏl interred his father in the So Mausoleum. The rites were conducted in an atmosphere of serenity such as Koryŏ had not known in many years. The last notes of the ceremonial dirge, however, became—or so it seemed—a signal for Mongol army officers and civil officials to surge into Kaegyŏng. Detachments of troops were again marching through the city. Residents of the capital were at first puzzled, then became alarmed, for they saw only Mongol and Chinese soldiers. There were no Koreans among them.

*

The combined invasion force of twenty-five thousand troops set sail from Happ'o on October 3. The harbor was a deep inlet that resembled a long narrow lake when seen from the hills that rose from the coast. That slender body of water was filled with war vessels by noon. The nine hundred crafts remained stationary for several hours, then in the late afternoon their number began gradually to diminish. But when darkness descended upon the waters, that number had reverted to the original nine hundred. After nightfall, the winds acquired the force of a gale. The women of fishing villages near Happ'o predicted to one another that the sailing would be postponed for two or three days. But at the first light of the next dawn not one vessel was seen in the narrow inlet.

At Kaegyŏng, from October 3 on, every Buddhist monastery tolled its large bell at dawn and dusk, sending forth prayers to ensure the safe return of every soldier and ship. The people of Koryŏ listened to the tolling of the bells with feelings that were mixed. They prayed for the safe return of all ships carrying Koreans, but were not inclined to offer similar prayers for the safety of the Mongols and the Chinese.

It was rumored around that time that Princess Khutlgaimish would soon come to Koryŏ. This rumor was of greater interest to the women and old men of Kaegyŏng than news about the army of conquest.

King Ch'ungnyŏl had despatched Ki On, the assistant commissioner of military affairs, to Yen-tu to serve as the Mongol princess's escort. Princess Khutlgaimish was scheduled to arrive in Koryŏ in early October, but her party seemed to be traveling at a very leisurely pace. Each of the four couriers sent back by Ki On specified a date of arrival later than that in the previous report. The last stated that the princess had crossed the Yalu River. King Ch'ungnyŏl set out for the northwest to meet her. On the twenty-fourth he arrived at Sŏgyŏng and, on the twenty-fifth, greeted her as her party approached a small town on the plains north of Sŏgyŏng. Traveling together, the king and the Mongol princess arrived in Kaegyŏng on the fifth day of November.

The royal consorts and the wives of all princes of the blood and high ministers were dressed in ceremonial finery when they assembled outside the northern boundary of the capital. The ministers and courtiers stood in rows before the gate of the Hukch'ŏng Mon-

astery, where they greeted the Mongol princess's train. Khutlgaimish had the procession stop and she dismounted whenever she
encountered a group of well-wishers, assuming that to be the proper
gesture. The onlookers' curiosity would focus at first on the exotic
design of the Tartar carriage, but they caught their breath when the
princess alighted on the ground. It was not only her beauty that
astonished them but her youth—she was a young girl of sixteen.

King Ch'ungnyŏl bade her enter his royal carriage, and together
they rode into Kaegyŏng. As they were riding through the capital,
the princess stopped the procession and stepped down onto the
street. Although this was not customary in his country, the king let
the young princess do as she wished. The boulevard was thronged
with residents hoping for a glimpse of the royal bride. Khutlgaimish
glanced only briefly at the multitude, then scanned the sky overhead
and turned her gaze wistfully to the tiled roofs of the Buddhist
monasteries in the far distance.

The people felt a sudden surge of emotion as they observed the
princess, who was willing to be seen by them. Never before had
they seen such an innocent display of royalty. Some of the old men
clung to each other, sharing a sentiment that moved them to tears.
A few fell to the ground and wept openly, thinking that perhaps the
era of Mongol depredation had at last ended. One onlooker composed a salutation to the princess. He stopped writing frequently to
wipe the tears that coursed down his cheeks, but could not stem
their flow. Standing at the roadside, he brushed a long message of
welcome, which began: "Never did I expect to witness an era of
peace after 'the century of slashing blades and whistling arrows.' "

When the royal carriage entered the palace gate, the princess's
Mongol escort, T'o-hu, stretched out a cloth canopy and purified it
ritually with lamb oil. The Koryŏ officials regarded the exotic rite
with curiosity, somewhat alarmed by the intrusion into their palace
of an alien custom. King Ch'ungnyŏl's consort, Queen Chŏngsin,
that day changed her name to Chŏnghwa and moved into separate
palatial quarters; thenceforth she and the king would not see each
other.

Some twenty days after Princess Khutlgaimish's arrival in Koryŏ,
twelve war vessels sailed into Happ'o harbor, basking in the deep

crimson cast by the sky at sunset. Their hulls were badly damaged, and their masts were broken almost uniformly at mid-height. The first ship to dock disgorged several dozen Mongol soldiers. They were drawn and haggard, many of them were injured. The third ship brought Hong Tagu, who promptly assembled all the men on the shore, ordered them to remain stationary, and then strode off to the next ship that was docking.

Hong Tagu inspected the men as they disembarked and segregated them according to physical characteristics. The number of Koreans was pitifully small.

Dozens of bonfires lit the shore that night, but no more vessels came. In the morning two more ships returned, both as badly damaged as the others. Kim Pang-gyŏng came ashore from one of them and was promptly confronted by Hong Tagu, who asked him if the construction of the war vessels might not have been faulty. Tagu said that he had been skeptical about the capability of ships of Korean design. Kim turned and walked away. But Hong Tagu caught up with him and said accusingly that it must have been the inexperience of the Korean seamen that had been the major cause of the disaster. Again Kim did not answer. He was preoccupied with thoughts of helping his people survive the oncoming winter. The land of Koryŏ, its forests denuded of trees, all of its fields deserted by able-bodied men, presented a picture of misery far more pitiful than that of a defeated army. Koryŏ had fulfilled its obligation to Kubilai. Kim felt driven by an urgency to devote his life, which the stormy sea had spared, to help the people of Koryŏ sustain their lives. Although he did not know how many of the fifteen thousand Koreans may have survived the expedition, he was certain that the majority had perished.

News of the disastrous expedition—thirteen thousand five hundred of the original twenty-five thousand men killed or drowned, most of the war vessels destroyed—reached King Ch'ungnyŏl in Kaegyŏng in early December. Then the commanders returned—Kim Pang-gyŏng first, followed at intervals of two to three days by Hong Tagu, Liu Fu-heng, and Hindu.

On January 4, the Mongol commanders left Kaegyŏng for Yentu. Four days later, Kim Pang-gyŏng also left to seek an audience with Kubilai. He had not been summoned. He intended to describe his people's misery and plead for their release from the obligation to provide food for the remnants of the Yuan army still garrisoned in Koryŏ.

During the first month of 1275, with the concurrence of his court, King Ch'ungnyŏl modified the administrative structure of Koryŏ and changed the titles of government officials to conform closely to those used by the Yuan government. He also ordered his courtiers to style their hair as the Mongols did. Although he had urged them to do so a month earlier, only a few had complied. His court was now agreeable. He suggested that those men who had accompanied him earlier and had lived among the Mongols as hostages be assigned to a new office to be called *horchi*. His court was again agreeable. These measures, the king believed, would facilitate Koryŏ's recovery. He visualized Khutlgaimish's girlish face and thought of her not merely as his queen, but as a newly acquired magical charm that would invigorate Koryŏ. The war of conquest, the cause of many years' suffering, was over. Koryŏ was on the threshold of a path of endeavor which, under the leadership of a new king, would lead her out of the depths of deprivation.

BOOK TWO

CHAPTER 1

THE UNCHECKED flight of Koryŏ's people northward became a grave problem for the government following the 1274 expedition. When Ch'oe T'an had delivered himself to the Mongols in 1270, together with the sixty cities in the territories of the northern border and the western seas, that part of Koryŏ north of Chabi Pass, one-fourth of its entire land, had been annexed by the Yuan Empire. Sŏgyŏng, formerly the western capital of Koryŏ, had been renamed Tongnyŏng-pu and was now the eastern headquarters for Yuan government offices and armies.

With the Yuan army of occupation ever present, the people could not foresee an end to the exactions imposed on them and, in fact, talked of worse times to come when another Yuan expedition would be sent to conquer Japan. Although they knew next to nothing about living conditions outside Koryŏ, they assumed that an escape into Yuan territory would bring release from taxation and conscription for military service and corvée labor. Dozens, at times hundreds, of Koreans drifted northward daily.

Lamenting this, Pak Yu, the chancellor of the treasury, recommended in February of 1275 that members of Koryŏ's upper classes take wives from among the commoners—in other words, practice polygamy to help their women bear many children and repopulate a country that had an abundance of widows and spinsters but very few males. The custom of polygamy was not adopted. If it had been, its lure would not have sufficed to keep the people bound to their lands. That such an outrageous idea would have merited any discussion at all bespoke the gravity of the problem of depopulation at a time less than six months after the overseas debacle.

On February 29, a contingent of fourteen hundred Chinese troops formerly of the army of the Sung Empire arrived in Kaegyŏng and were promptly divided into three units for assignment in Yomju, Haeju, and Paekchu, cities which in 1271 had been designated zones for Yuan colonization. The government of Koryŏ was caught by surprise, for it had expected the military colonies to be abolished after the abortive war of conquest. The men who governed Koryŏ had not dismissed the possibility of another Mongol attempt to conquer Japan, but they had expected the Mongols to wait until the injuries recently sustained by Koryŏ had fully healed. The arrival of new colonial troops upset their complacency.

On the following day, Kim Pang-gyŏng's first letter from Yen-tu was delivered to Koryŏ's capital. King Ch'ungnyŏl summoned the courier into his presence at once.

"Tu Shih-ch'ung and Ho Wen-chu, envoys for the admonition of Japan, have recently been despatched from Yen-tu and are scheduled to arrive in Kaegyŏng."

Even as the courier read Kim's letter, the king sprang up from his cushion. Up on one knee, he held that position to maintain steadiness, for the earth suddenly seemed to have begun to pitch and roll. The Yuan Empire was sending envoys to Japan again! The dread that suffused the entire being of Koryŏ's new king was inspired by his realization that Emperor Kubilai's rapacious gaze was fixed ever steadily on Japan.

Tu Shih-ch'ung, deputy director of the Bureau of Military Affairs, and Ho Wen-chu, deputy director of the Bureau of Ritual Affairs, came to Kaegyŏng on March 10. Even though King Ch'ungnyŏl had been forewarned of their arrival, the actual presence of Yuan envoys bound for Japan so soon after the war unnerved him.

The king had earlier entrusted Kim Pang-gyŏng with this memorial for delivery to Kubilai:

Because of the need recently to clear the land of the rebellious Sambyŏlch'o Elite Corps, every household in my modest nation contributed food and fodder to sustain a great army. During the subsequent war to conquer Japan, my people built war vessels, and almost all of our able-bodied were levied to assist in the war, leaving only the aged and enfeebled to tend the fields. First came the drought, then the floods, and there were no crops. The needs of the military were met by my impoverished people, who contributed food in single piculs and even smaller units. Already some subsist on nuts, grasses, and leaves. Never before have my people been so stricken with poverty. Many of our men were felled by injury or caught in the deep waters, and did not return. My people continue to respire, but cannot be expected to regain their vigor within a few short months or years. Should war again be made on Japan, my modest nation could not possibly provide adequate assistance. We no longer possess so much as a single otter pelt. And we are unable to remedy our want. Cast your gaze on us, O Heaven, for you have neglected us! I prostrate myself, hoping that my sincerity and piteous pleas may receive due recognition.

Kubilai's response to this memorial was to despatch his emissaries to admonish Japan.

The king held a banquet to fete the envoy Tu Shih-ch'ung, the vice envoy Ho Wen-chu, the envoys' counselor Suturjin, who was an Arab by birth, and Hua-teng, a Uighur serving as the mission's scribe. Envoy Tu was a man in his mid-thirties, some twenty years younger than his subaltern. Just as the banquet was approaching its height of festivity, clouds suddenly gathered overhead, thunder reverberated across the heavens, and hail the size of a man's fist pounded the earth amid rain that fell in sheets. Lamps were brought into the hall to lift the midday darkness, and the banquet was continued despite the din of hailstones pounding the tiled roof. This banquet, the sixth at which the court of Koryŏ feted Mongol emissaries bound for Japan, was unusually dreary. Neither the guests nor the hosts spoke much. When Sŏ Ch'an heard the the king announce his appointment as interpreter with the rank of commander for assignment to the mission, inexplicably he rose to his feet and performed a dance transmitted from ancient times in his native South Kyŏngsang province. The dance itself was somber. Sŏ Ch'an, his singing muted by the deafening resonance of the hail and his slowly moving dancing figure dimly lit by lamplight, presented an image at best gloomy. During the storm the south gate of the royal palace was struck by lightning.

The Yuan envoy's party of some one dozen men left Kaegyŏng two days later for Happ'o, whence it would set sail for Japan, its ranks increased to about thirty by a complement of Korean naval personnel. King Ch'ungnyŏl bade the travelers farewell at the partially destroyed south gate and sent a group of courtiers to escort the Yuan envoy as far as the Han River. The mission was much smaller than that which Chao Liang-pi had headed four years earlier. King Ch'ungnyŏl could not predict how the Japanese would receive the Yuan envoy so soon after the invasion, nor could he foresee the future that was being shaped by Kubilai's unnatural fascination with Japan.

On July 25, Ho-te, the *darughachi* in Kaegyŏng, was recalled to his homeland. Ho-te had first come to Kangdo a decade earlier, at which time he took his Mongol party as far as Kŏje Island before turning back. On his third mission in 1272 he reached Kyushu. After returning from Japan he traveled frequently between Yuan and Koryŏ, much involved in the affairs of the two nations. He had been the resident *darughachi* in Kaegyŏng since King Wŏnjong's death. Without doubt the most knowledgeable among Yuan experts on Koryŏ, he had been considered by many Koreans to be a very unusual Yuan official who worked both overtly and behind the scenes to protect Koryŏ. But Koryŏ's new king disliked Ho-te. Ch'ungnyŏl wished to assert his kingship, to let it be known that the era of King Wŏnjong had passed. For no purpose other than to relieve Koryŏ of Yuan depredation had he wedded Kubilai's daughter and adopted Tartar apparel and hairstyle. He could not forget the sharp look of disapprobation in his father's eyes the first time he appeared before him attired and coiffured as a Mongol. He thought he detected the same reproving look in Ho-te's eyes. Ho-te had been sent by the Yuan Empire to be the senior administrator of its tributary state, and his manifest inclination to favor Koryŏ's retention of its intrinsic values seemed something of a contradiction. He may have disdained King Ch'ungnyŏl for adopting Mongol customs to replace Koryŏ's own and modifying Koryŏ's governmental structure to conform to that of the Yuan Empire. The king felt certain that he did. Although no visible conflict marred the relationship between the two, people detected a discord between them and they often talked about it.

In September, the swordsmith Ku-nei arrived from Yen-tu, and in November a Yuan emissary came with orders for Koryŏ to produce weapons. The king bade the royal secretary Kim Che accompany the emissary to Kyŏngsang and Chŏlla provinces to levy feathers and pig iron for the production of arrows.

These recent events suggesting a renewed Mongol interest in conquering Japan unnerved the people, who had been looking to the future with trepidation. The northward migration of farmers could not be stemmed despite a stringent ban imposed by the government. A touch of brightness was lent to the prevalent gloom when Queen Khutlgaimish delivered a baby prince on September 30. All the lords and courtiers gathered at the palace, and rejoicing city dwellers formed crowds outside the four palace gates to celebrate the happy event. The prince, named Wŏn, would later become King Ch'ungsŏn.

In December, Chang Kuo-kang arrived in Kaegyŏng to replace Ho-te as *darughachi;* with him came the assistant *darughachi* Shih-mo T'ien-chü. Chang, a man in his fifties, was gracious of manner and speech. Shih-mo T'ien-chü, somewhat younger than Chang, was taciturn and humorless and said to be a stickler in matters of regulation and procedure. Both were in Koryŏ for the first time. Although their unfamiliarity with the country and its people was bound to create difficulties, King Ch'ungnyŏl preferred them to Ho-te.

On January 20 of the new year, 1276, the court of Koryŏ received a wholly unexpected edict from Kubilai: stop building ships and make no more arrows. The surprised king could only conclude that Kubilai had heeded his recent plea, or had called off the invasion.

One of Koryŏ's courtiers despatched to offer New Year's congratulations to the Yuan court arrived back in Kaegyŏng in early March. He had not known about the order to suspend the production of arms. He described what he had heard and seen: remnants of the Chinese army in the Sung capital, Lin-an, had at last capitulated; news of the final victory had the entire city of Yen-tu in frenzied jubilation.

Kim Pang-gyŏng left Kaegyŏng a fortnight later to deliver the king's congratulatory message, and in early May he was received in audience by Kubilai at Shang-tu, the western capital. The charged ambience within the palace grounds, he learned, was due to the anticipation that the vanquished Sung generals would be coming to pay Kubilai homage. Kim was surprised to learn that Kubilai was to receive the vanquished generals with benign forgiveness.

Kim remained in Shang-tu for a month. He was unwilling to leave without knowing whether Kubilai would again try to conquer Japan. Kubilai's order to suspend the production of arms might be considered prophetic. When he first issued the order, the Mongols were engaged in an ostensibly drawn out war with the Sung. Because the walled city of Hsiang-yang had withstood a siege for six years, Kubilai could not have expected the Sung capital, Lin-an, to fall quickly. But Lin-an had been taken with surprising ease in January. Now that the great war with the Sung was over, what new conquests was Kubilai contemplating? Kim needed to know, but propriety forbade his addressing that question directly to the Yuan emperor.

At the beginning of May, the vanquished Sung generals Hsia Kuei, Lu Wen-huan, Ch'en I, and Fan Wen-hu arrived in Shang-tu and presented themselves to their conqueror, Kubilai. Kim Panggyŏng, summoned for this occasion, was seated in a place that honored him above the Sung generals, whose illustrious names he knew well. Generals Ch'en, Fan, and Lu had surrendered in 1275, and Hsia Kuei after the fall of Lin-an. Kubilai conversed amiably with his longtime foes, inquiring of their places of birth and their families. Ch'en, Fan, and Lu said that they had lost their immediate families at the time of their surrender in 1275. Kubilai then had the generals describe the strategies they had used during the long war. Their vivid descriptions of the siege of Hsiang-yang impressed upon their audience the fury of the many battles in which victories and defeats had been shared alike by the contending armies.

Three of the generals spoke, but Fan Wen-hu did not, insisting that he recalled nothing that might interest the listeners. Prodded by Kubilai, the short, portly general narrated a story about failure: when Hsiang-yang was besieged by the army of the Yuan general Aju and appeared to be in danger of falling, he had been ordered by the Sung emperor to lead an army to the walled city's rescue; while carousing, however, he brought singing girls into the encampment and became so drunk that his army failed to attack, as a result of which the Sung forces lost their tactical advantage and Hsiang-yang fell; though he should have been charged with negligence and executed, he was most fortunate in merely being relieved of command and appointed prefect of An-ch'ing.

There was an outburst of laughter as he finished. Kubilai laughed, and so too did the three Sung generals. Fan Wen-hu shrugged his shoulders in embarrassment. Drollery had not been his intent. His selection of that particular anecdote and his utter frankness revealed something of the character of this fifty-year-old general whose name had for many years symbolized courage and ferocity even among the Mongols.

Kubilai then bade Yelü Hsi-liang recount the history of the Yuan endeavor to subjugate Japan and, when Yelü had finished, turned to the Sung generals.

"Shall I attack Japan?" he asked in a voice suddenly become resonant, "or shall I not?" Each of them replied respectfully that the empire should attack Japan.

"Will it be an easy conquest or will it not?" Kubilai asked. Hsia Kuei, Lu Wen-huan, and Ch'en I replied one after the other, "I believe it will be an easy conquest."

Fan Wen-hu alone dissented. "Extensive preparations will be required," he said. "Unless the attack is made with an army several times larger than the one before, the result again will be failure. Victory will not come easily in any war fought across the sea." His eyes, set in an almost jocular face, narrowed as he spoke.

"How many years will such preparations require?" Kubilai asked. Fan Wen-hu inclined his head to one side several times as he pondered the question, but ultimately did not answer.

"I too have an opinion." Yelü Hsi-liang spoke out as if to end the lull. "The three empires, Sung, Liao, and Chin, each wishing to reign supreme, kept this part of the world in a state of continuous war for three hundred years. The country needs a respite from war. The difference between bringing Japan into the fold of the Yuan Empire right now or a few years hence does not seem all that important."

Yelü Hsi-liang was the great-grandson of Yelü Ch'u-ts'ai, who had served the great khans Jenghis and Ogodei well in the building of the Mongol empire. Yelü Hsi-liang's remark told Kim Pang-gyŏng what he had wished to know. Kubilai intended to invade Japan again, this time with the aid of Chinese commanders and troops. Several days later, Kim Pang-gyŏng presented himself at the palace to take his leave of Kubilai. The emperor took the occasion of Kim's departure from Shang-tu to recognize his valorous services to the Yuan Empire. He bestowed upon him the gold escutcheon displaying the heraldic tiger's head, making Kim the first soldier from the Korean peninsula ever to receive a gold escutcheon of the Middle Kingdom.

Returning to Kaegyŏng in June, Kim Pang-gyŏng conveyed to King Ch'ungnyŏl what he had heard and observed in Shang-tu. The Mongol Empire will again invade Japan, this time with forces consisting principally of Chinese troops of the former Sung Empire. He was quite certain, he added, that the effect on Koryŏ would not be calamitous.

A few days after that, a directive from the Yuan secretariat ordered Koryŏ to resume the production of arrows. The royal court puzzled over the fact that the edict specified only arrows, and did not mention war vessels. The pessimists among the courtiers said that the order presaged darker times to come, whereas the majority believed the edict to be an augury of the lifting of darkness. Some attributed the surprisingly light burden to the fact that Princess Khutlgaimish's marriage had created a familial bond between Koryŏ and the Yuan Empire. Others said that Kubilai, cognizant of the great suffering inflicted on them during the earlier invasion, had assigned them a token task whose fulfillment would satisfy the least obligation of a tributary state.

King Ch'ungnyŏl was happy to comply with the order to make arrows, though even this minor assignment would tax his debilitated country.

On October 13, a Yuan emissary arrived with a rescript from Kubilai summoning King Ch'ungnyŏl and his queen to the Yuan court in May of the following year. Khutlgaimish had not been home since her marriage. The news of the king and queen's traveling together to the court of Emperor Kubilai gladdened all of

Koryŏ's officialdom. The king promptly despatched an emissary with a message of compliance and, after a few days' interval, another bearing an offering of chestnuts. When Chao Liang-pi had returned from his first mission to Japan, he had brought back saplings of the chestnut tree. King Wonjong had them planted in a village in the mountainous district of Ŭian, whose climate was said to resemble that of Japan. The saplings had grown into sturdy trees and now had yielded their first crop of chestnuts, and King Ch'ungnyŏl had thought to present some to Emperor Kubilai.

The northward migration of Koreans ceased altogether in autumn. The year had been one without natural calamities, and the harvest, though less than bountiful, yielded far more rice than in any recent year. Cheerfulness was again evident in the villages, and no one doubted that conditions in Koryŏ were gradually improving.

*

As the year 1276 was drawing to a close, an untoward occurrence brought great consternation to the court of Koryŏ. The following letter, brushed in cultured calligraphy, was delivered anonymously on the night of December 16 to the residence of the assistant *darughachi* Shih-mo T'ien-chü: "Having been deprived of the king's affection, Queen Chŏnghwa has had a shaman place a curse on Queen Khutlgaimish. Also, forty-three courtiers, including the lord of Chean Prince Suk, Chief Minister Kim Pang-gyŏng, Pak Hang, Yi Ch'ang-gyŏng, Yi Punhŭi, and Yi Punsŏng, have conspired to escape to Kanghwa Island."

All six men named in the accusation were apprehended by Yuan troops in less than two hours. Before dawn the following morning, Queen Chŏnghwa was removed from her detached palace at the order of Khutlgaimish, placed in confinement within the royal palace, and forbidden access to her possessions. The officials who took charge of incarcerating Queen Chŏnghwa were Yin-hou, Chang Shun-lung, and Che Hsin, three among those men who had come to Koryŏ as Khutlgaimish's personal attendants, or *kelinkou*, and whose flaunting of authority had quickly alienated the Koreans.

The seventeenth was the day of the month when all the ministers of Koryŏ gathered at the residence of the *darughachi* to discuss matters of state. Only one of the Korean ministers present knew what had taken place the night before. Shih-mo T'ien-chü made no mention of it.

"Spring is near," he said. "I should like to engage all of you in a contest of poetry with the hope that at least one of our poems might aptly express the joy of welcoming spring."

The minister Yu Kyŏng, who at sixty-five was the same age as Kim Pang-gyŏng, had been privy to the past night's happenings.

"Our queen and chief minister are restrained by tether," he said, his voice quivering in anger, "and you consider this to be a suitable time for singing songs!"

Leaving the *darughachi*'s residence, Yu Kyŏng hastened directly to the king's chamber. Khutlgaimish had been raging: she objected to King Ch'ungnyŏl's calling her "my Mongol guest" rather than "my queen" and had repeatedly screamed, "Your Mongol guest will take her baby and go back to her own country!"

"This king of this tiny nation has just managed to quiet his queen," King Ch'ungnyŏl explained with a chortle though wearing a look of distress. Yu had heard a rumor of the king's inability to contend with Khutlgaimish's petulance, and now he knew that rumor to be true.

With the king's permission, Yu proceeded to the Kyongsong Palace to meet with Queen Khutlgaimish. When the queen and her attendants appeared, Yu dropped to his knees and, in that humble posture, progressed into her near presence.

"Once, not so long ago, a few powerful vassals gained control of the nation's government," Yu said, "and there followed a proliferation of slander. Then came years of disorder. Men were punished before charges lodged against them could be verified. They were executed in as great numbers as the reed stalks felled every autumn by reapers. Officials, even commoners, lived in such fear that they were grateful to be alive when night fell or the next day dawned. The glorious might of the Yuan Empire swept the renegades into oblivion so that you, Imperial Princess, could progress to this eastern nation to become its queen. We subjects rejoiced, for we believed that our nation would never again be subjected to adversity. And yet we are stricken with adversity.

"Listen to my explanation of that anonymous letter. Our people are impoverished. Contingents of the Yuan imperial army are garrisoned everywhere in Koryŏ. Who would dare flee the land, much less hatch unconscionable plots? If we should believe the allegations in that anonymous letter and punish the accused, we would then wonder if we might not be the next victims of similar slander. We would be robbed of the peace of mind that enables us to serve you wholeheartedly. The allegation of Queen Chŏnghwa practicing sorcery is a simple lie that even a child would not believe. Your coming to Koryŏ as King Ch'ungnyŏl's queen brought tranquility to our people, for they were made aware of your imperial father's virtues. If Queen Chŏnghwa had indeed placed a curse on you, the gods would already have punished her for having violated their injunctions. No one born in Koryŏ would fail to understand this . . ."

Shaken with tears, Yu Kyŏng could not continue. But what he said touched everyone to the core.

The seventeen-year-old queen, her sensitive face pale and hardened, had kept her unblinking eyes fixed on the aged minister.

"Release the men, but not Chŏnghwa," she said in a clear, high-pitched voice.

When Yu raised his head, Khutlgaimish had begun to retreat to the inner chamber. Yu sprang to his feet, raced up behind her, and prostrated himself, reaching out as if to grasp the hem of her robe. Again he pleaded on Queen Chŏnghwa's behalf as Khutlgaimish looked down on him.

"Release the queen, too," she said, with no discernible change in her expression. It seemed as if only the tiny mouth in her slender, almost childlike face had moved. Some moments passed before Yu realized that Khutlgaimish had uttered the word "release" rather than the dreaded "execute." He remained prostrated, his head touching the floor, repeating words of gratitude and weeping audibly. Prince Suk, Kim Pang-gyŏng, and the other four men were released from prison that day, and Queen Chŏnghwa also had her freedom restored.

The unfortunate incident was thus resolved. Although there were no repercussions, those who knew what had taken place began to foresee a beclouded future for Koryŏ. The writer of the slanderous letter was never identified, and the court of Koryŏ learned that any act of malicious mischief could easily precipitate a national crisis. It had seen its nation's vulnerability exposed.

The courtiers and officials of Koryŏ now knew that Shih-mo T'ien-chü, with whom many held amiable converse almost daily, would have any of them thrown into prison on the basis of hearsay. Among the Koreans who had been imprisoned on his orders were a prince of the blood and a general who had received the gold escutcheon from Emperor Kubilai. Although Shih-mo was Chang Kuo-k'ang's assistant, he had been rumored to be the *darughachi* with executive authority. The truth of that rumor was confirmed by this untoward incident, which originated in Shih-mo's residence and was inflated wholly out of proportion at Shih-mo's whim.

The court of Koryŏ also learned that the *darughachi* was much more than an office of a resident commissioner who transmitted Yuan instructions to the Koryŏ government and acted on orders from its own government. It was empowered to issue orders on its own initiative. The office of the *darughachi* had suddenly become an intimidating presence.

On the eighth day following the incident, King Ch'ungnyŏl despatched an emissary to the Yuan secretariat bearing a document describing the case of slander. His vassals had urged him to submit an accurate account, for they could not be sure how the *darughachi* might have described the same events in his report to Kubilai:

Talk of imprecation is inspired by ignorance. The mirrored light of Imperial emanation will illumine the truth for all to see. Your *darughachi* has shown me an anonymous letter that tells of more than forty men congregating to plot a return to Kanghwa Island. If that information had been true and based on evidence, it would have been properly disclosed and reported in a forthright manner, not secretly by an unnamed dissembler whose only purpose was to fabricate lies to vent his resentment against the nation or against certain individuals. In the list of more than forty names is that of a Korean who has been dead for five years. Is that not proof of the intent to slander? I seek your enlightened judgment and ask that you take no notice hereafter of missives composed by unnamed persons.

No sooner had the new year, 1277, arrived than gossip of the recent case of slander spread quickly through Kaegyŏng. The populace was fascinated particularly because Princess Khutlgaimish had had a principal role in the affair. They were reminded of their king's having two consorts—Queen Chŏnghwa and Khutlgaimish, whose formal title was Queen Wŏnsŏng. They learned that Queen Chŏnghwa had lived apart from the king since the day Khutlgaimish arrived—indeed a logical arrangement that would preclude disharmony. But they understood, too, that logic alone could not prevent such complications in human affairs as had led to the recent unhappy events.

Gossip circulated such tattle as: King Ch'ungnyŏl was so dominated by the Yuan princess that he sought her approval on all matters; Khutlgaimish was possessed of such intense jealousy that the king dared not be seen near Queen Chŏnghwa's detached palace; Khutlgaimish had plotted the incident in an attempt to eliminate Queen Chŏnghwa and her supporters.

The behavior of those *kelinkou*, Yin-hou, Chang Shun-lung, and Che Hsin, came under public scrutiny. Yin-hou was a Mongol, and Chang Shun-lung an Arab by birth. Che Hsin was a Korean who had been raised in Mongolia. Upon arriving in Koryŏ as members of Princess Khutlgaimish's entourage, they had adopted Korean surnames, gained important offices through the princess's influence, vied with one another for power, and indulged without shame in every extravagance. Each maintained a conspicuously opulent residence in the capital. Chang's, in particular, was surrounded by a high wall built of fine stone and topped with the finest tile cast in floral designs. Their role in apprehending the queen made them objects of great resentment among the people, who said that Khutlgaimish, young and often naive, was a woman of good character who suffered the misfortune of being surrounded by noxious attendants.

Except for often-far-fetched speculations on the identity of the nameless writer of that letter, popular gossip tended to sum up the true state of affairs with surprising accuracy.

On January 24, a Yuan emissary arrived in Kaegyŏng with Kubilai's injunction forbidding the possession of bows and arrows by Koreans. According to the emissary, Emperor Kubilai had been informed of the case of slander even before he received the report from the court of Koryŏ and had issued this emergency ban on weapons to forestall violence. Furthermore, the Yuan government had taken an extraordinary measure to quell the growing disquiet in Koryŏ: it had appointed Hong Tagu supreme commander of the Army for the Pacification of Koryŏ and Subjugation of the East.

King Ch'ungnyŏl paled at the mention of Hong Tagu, a detested name he had almost forgotten. He and his father, the late King Wŏnjong, had differed in temperament and in their approaches to solving problems of nationhood and, indeed, problems of life itself. But they had been in agreement with regard to the Yuan general Hong Tagu, a man who flouted every dictate of Heaven. The king felt only loathing whenever he recalled the colorless face of the young general, a pure-blooded Korean who flayed the people of Koryŏ, never wincing as even commanders of Mongol blood must have at times at the sight of the cruelty they inflicted on the Koreans. Hong Tagu would return, wielding even greater power and authority to meddle in the affairs of Koryŏ.

No less dismayed by the prospect of Hong Tagu's return was the senior minister Kim Pang-gyŏng. Having worked closely with him while supervising the construction of warships during the preparatory stages of the invasion, then during the invasion as coequal commanders, Kim of all Koreans knew him best.

"Hong Tagu has reached middle age. and probably recognizes his past vainglory as a folly of youth," Kim said. "We should remember that he is a Korean by birth and shares our blood. I doubt that he would be unreasonable if we approach him with sincerity and solicitude."

Kim Pang-gyŏng counseled placation lest his king and fellow courtiers antagonize Hong Tagu through a display of excessive wariness. But Kim himself was convinced that Hong Tagu had not changed. He often thought of Tagu, and whenever he did he would see Kubilai's face behind that of Tagu. He had come to recognize this recurring image as a symbol of his belief that Kubilai's every will was manifested through Hong Tagu's utterance. It was as though some living part of Kubilai resided in the person of Hong Tagu. Hong Tagu was an intricately crafted marionette dangling at the end of strings held in Kubilai's hands, and he could not be bargained with because puppets were not endowed with the ability to reason.

But there was another possibility—that Hong Tagu intuitively perceived Kubilai's wishes and determined his own actions to conform
unerringly with the presumed imperial wishes. If the latter was the
case, Hong Tagu was a fiercely loyal, sensitive, efficient vassal of
Kubilai. Which of the two was Hong Tagu? Kim was not sure. But
he knew that Kubilai's ubiquitous presence had to be taken into
consideration in evaluating any action undertaken by Hong Tagu.

Kubilai greatly fascinated Kim Pang-gyŏng. He was a monarch of
surpassing ability, with a grand vision that admitted no trivialities.
But he was also a shrewd conqueror who relegated the brutal tasks
of subjugation to men like Hong Tagu. Although the prideful Tagu
was a detestable sort, he deserved admiration for his competence as a
soldier who carried out those tasks efficiently. His coming to Koryŏ
as the supreme military commander meant that Kubilai's will, now
firmer than ever, would be manifested in ways they could not predict. And they could not expect Hong Tagu to be generous.

Because the ban on private ownership of bows and arrows had
been issued by Kubilai, King Ch'ungnyŏl ordered that every village
in the land assign one person to be charged with the responsibility of
gathering up weapons. But the ban deprived hunters of their means
of livelihood and would have to be repealed, or at least modified.
The king thought to enter a plea during his forthcoming audience
with Kubilai in May.

A message from the Yuan secretariat, received at the end of January, reminded Koryŏ of the quantity of arrows it must produce no
later than the last day in February. In quick succession similar
reminders were received from the *darughachi* in Kaegyŏng and the
colonial administrator of Sŏkchu. In view of the apparent urgency,
the king sent inspectors to all the provinces to insure against any
slackening of effort.

On February 14, the courtier Chu Yŏl, who had been in Shang-tu
to congratulate Kubilai on New Year's day, returned to Kaegyŏng
with intriguing news. Sisik, Tutum, and other members of Mongol
royalty had raised a rebellion in the northern desert region, and
General Derwatai, stationed at the northern fringe of the empire,
had cast his lot with the rebels. Shang-tu was in an uproar, with
Mongol troops and units made up of Jurchens, Chinese, and expa-

triate Koreans moving in and out of the capital daily. King Ch'ungnyŏl promptly convened his ministers. At one point in the discussion, consensus favored sending Kim Pang-gyŏng's son, Kim Hŭn,
at the head of a Korean army to aid the Yuan Empire. Ultimately
they decided to wait for instructions from Kubilai. They hoped that
the uprising was a minor one and would be put down quickly, for
the cost of despatching a large expeditionary force would be prohib-
itive.

Two days later, the senior colonel No Yong also returned from
Shang-tu. No Yong, originally from the Western Marches of China,
had come to Koryŏ as Princess Khutlgaimish's personal attendant.
Unlike the three despised *kelinkou,* he was a man of honesty and
gentle disposition. He informed the king that Hong Tagu, soon to
leave for Koryŏ, had been ordered to the battlefront. Also sent into
battle at Kubilai's command was the unit of five hundred expatriate
Koreans which had been garrisoned in that part of northern Koryŏ
annexed by the Mongols. "This is fortunate for you," said No
Yong.

The turbulence within the Yuan Empire brought Koryŏ two
blessings. First, the removal of the five-hundred-strong unit of expatriate Koreans from the annexed territory was an unqualified blessing, for those men were maintained wholly at the expense of the
people of Koryŏ. The second was possibly an even greater blessing.
The postponement of the coming of a great army commanded by
Hong Tagu gave Koryŏ time and an opportunity to have Tagu's
orders revoked. The king hoped that the rebellion would keep
Hong Tagu committed to the battlefront long enough for Kubilai to
be advised of his error in assigning Tagu to Koryŏ. The more prolonged the rebellion, however, the greater the chances of Korean
troops being called on to support the Yuan army. The avoidance of
one adversity might well bring on the other.

On the last day of February, the government delivered the prescribed quantity of arrows to the colonial administration in Sokchu.
Kim Pang-gyŏng represented Koryŏ at the formal presentation of
the arrows to the chief administrator, Hindu.

That evening Hindu held a banquet in honor of Kim. During the
informal part of the proceedings, Hindu talked about the invasion

of Japan, which, although delayed because of the ongoing rebellion, would probably be carried out within two to three years.

"I have been in command of troops for six years, since I first came to your country in 1271," Hindu said. "Except for that brief foray into Japan, I have always lived among your people. King Wŏnjong has passed on. So too has the former chief minister Yi Chang-yong. Among the key officials of Koryŏ today, you are the one I know best. Fate has bound us together in a strange way. I have always had the role of delivering harsh orders to you and prodding you into compliance, and you have always been the one to explain, apologize, and appeal to me. Luckily, we have had few exchanges of that sort during the past year or two. But this period of harmony will soon end. I doubt that we shall have many more opportunities to enjoy each other's company in a relaxed setting. If the Yuan Empire should again attack Japan, I shall again be giving you orders and prodding you harshly into compliance."

Kim Pang-gyŏng had reasons to be grateful to Hindu, but also reasons to be resentful. Hindu was sympathetic to Koryŏ, a country he knew and understood well, and never failed to favor Koryŏ when he resolved problems over which he had judicial authority. Yet, whenever he was assigned tasks by the Mongol government, he spared no means, however harsh, to accomplish those tasks. Kim felt lifelong gratitude for Hindu's acceding to his plea to move the office of the colonial administration away from Pongju to reduce the distance over which grains had to be hauled from the provinces to the central granary. But he seethed with anger whenever he recalled Hindu's intransigence when, on the eve of the invasion of Japan, he had protested the impossibility of conscripting so many Koreans.

Later that evening, Kim Pang-gyŏng for the first time saw an inebriated Hindu. The wine had overtaken Hindu with suddenness. One moment he was speaking thoughtfully, and the next with abandon.

"You Koreans are no different from the Chinese," he said gruffly. "You think the world of the ancient Confucian Classics, and you worship the Buddha. And you look down on us Mongols. I'd wanted to say this to Yi Chang-yong but never found the opportunity to do so. What you Koreans say and what you actually think are two different things. You're no exception. The chief business of Mongols is conquest. And so Heaven detests us—or so you might think. But we all act according to the mandate of Heaven, and Heaven endowed the Mongol people with the will to conquer and kill. Why, then, would Heaven detest us? In the eyes of Heaven, we're not sinful. That's why we've been able to enslave you Koreans and the Chinese."

With some astonishment Kim Pang-gyŏng regarded Hindu. Wine had made him uncharacteristically arrogant. His loose talk must reveal something of his basic convictions, Pang-gyŏng thought. Yet he wondered if he should judge Hindu's character by what the wine had prompted him to say. If he did, he would have to conclude that even so estimable a Mongol as Hindu possessed a streak of obduracy. Regardless, he had seen Hindu display an inborn trait of the Mongol people, and was reminded again of the difficulties that arise when two peoples meet.

The rebellion in the Yuan Empire was not quelled as easily or quickly as King Ch'ungnyŏl had hoped. Officials arriving from Shang-tu described the capital congested with troops mobilized for a war that had no predictable end. Kubilai sent no directive to Koryŏ, and his continued silence, welcome to some, was a cause for alarm to others who feared an eventual order to provide a large support army. Many believed that Princess Khutlgaimish's marriage had elevated Koryŏ's status among the tributary nations and exempted it from exactions of troops and supplies; King Ch'ungnyŏl tended to think so. But Kim Pang-gyŏng could not subscribe to such optimism. He had suggested from the start that Koryŏ despatch an army to aid the Mongols; that Koryŏ and Yuan had been conjoined through the royal marriage, and if one encountered trouble the other should hasten to its assistance; and that it would be better to send a small army than no army at all, for supportive action would be a natural courtesy. He did not disclose his fear: that if Koryŏ did not placate Kubilai by despatching a body of troops, Kubilai might in his anger demand massive support.

Soon it was mid-March, and still there were no signs of the rebellion subsiding. The court, now nervous, accepted Kim Pang-gyŏng's urging and, at the end of the month, selected Pang-gyŏng's son, Kim Hŭn, to lead an army of several hundred men to assist the Yuan Empire. That army left Kaegyŏng in April.

In May, Chang Shun-lung returned from the Yuan court, bearing an edict from the secretariat addressed to King Ch'ungnyŏl. The edict stated that the rebellion in the northern plains would soon be crushed and Koryŏ was not to send its militia, whose assistance was not needed. Chang said that he had met Koryŏ's expeditionary force in the vicinity of Tung-ching, and those men would soon be back in Koryŏ.

The rebellion was not quelled as quickly as the Yuan Imperial Secretariat had predicted. In consequence, the travel of King Ch'ungnyŏl and Queen Khutlgaimish was postponed. Soon thereafter the people of Koryŏ heard about Hong Tagu's resounding victory over Derwatai's army at the Tora River. For this notable feat Hong Tagu was said to have been awarded fifty taels of silver, a golden saddle and stirrup, and a set of bow and arrows. Kim Panggyŏng saw the young general rising another rung toward the pinnacle of authority.

CHAPTER 2

THE REBELLION within the Yuan Empire was finally quelled in late autumn, but the respite from anguish which the Korean government had begun to enjoy was short-lived. In an indictment reminiscent of the case of slander a year earlier, Kim Pang-gyŏng and his son were accused of plotting an insurrection. The accusation, signed by the former marshal Wi Tŭgyu and the generals No Chinŭi and Kim Poktae, was delivered to Colonial Administrator Hindu on December 13. It contained seven charges:

First, three of Kim Pang-gyŏng's kin—his son Hŭn, son-in-law Cho Pyŏn, and adopted son Han Hŭiyu—and some four hundred others including Kong Yu, General Na Yu, An Sajŏng, and Kim Ch'ŏllok have plotted to assassinate the king and queen and the *darughachi,* flee to Kanghwa Island, and raise a rebellion against the Mongol Empire.

Second, although all implements of war should have reverted to the government following the invasion of Japan, Pang-gyŏng and members of his clan have retained arms in their possession.

Third, Pang-gyŏng has built war vessels, which lie at anchor at Pŏnnam and Konmi and off the coast of Chin Island, the intended rallying point for the populace.

Fourth, he has built a new residence in Koryu-dong, in close proximity to the residence of the *darughachi.*

Fifth, whereas the government had ordered the inhabitants of all islands to move away from shorelines, Pang-gyŏng and his son, in defiance of the order, have allowed them to dwell on coastal strips.

Sixth, at the time of the expedition Pang-gyŏng filled the ranks of navigators and seamen with men ignorant of naval warfare, thereby contributing to military failure.

148

Seventh, he has ordered his son Hŭn to defend Chinju, Chŏn Yu
to defend Kyŏngsan-pu, an adoptive son An Chŏkchae to take possession of Happ'o, and Han Hŭiyu to command the war vessels.

Hindu came to Kaegyŏng immediately with three hundred
mounted troops. Arriving at Kaegyŏng at dusk, he joined the assistant *darughachi* Shih-mo T'ien-ch'ü in a meeting with the king and
queen to describe the allegations.

All concerned parties had gathered at the palace by midnight.
"When a country is in decline, and the people hungry," Kim Pang-
gyŏng muttered as he took his seat, "their hearts become barren and
the result is unexpected grief." He sat quietly, visibly sullen, as did
his accusers, Wi Tŭgyu, No Chinŭi, and Kim Poktae, who were
aligned in a row opposite him. The ministers Yu Kyŏng and Wŏn Pu
were ordered to ascertain the truth in the presence of the king and
queen, Hindu, and Shih-mo T'ien-ch'ü.

Yu and Wŏn took turns questioning the principals in the un-
heated room. Kim Pang-gyŏng's raspy voice, barely audible as he
spoke haltingly, communicated the depth of the grief he felt.

The interrogation quickly revealed that the charges against Kim
Pang-gyŏng were groundless. Han Hŭiyu and others did indeed
possess weapons and stood accused of that particular charge, but
not Kim Pang-gyŏng. The accusers begged to be forgiven for their
rashness and explained that they had been driven by their extreme
concern for the nation. They gratuitously added words to the effect
that the clearing of suspicion was a cause for rejoicing on behalf of
Minister Kim and the nation.

Kim remained silent, overwhelmed by a heaviness of heart such as
he had never known. He had dedicated his lifetime of sixty-seven
years to his country, only to become an object of resentment, to be
humiliated. Why would his countrymen wish to degrade him? The
accusers, all occupants of important posts, had at one time or
another been his subordinates—Wi Tŭgyu during the invasion of
Japan, and No Chinŭi and Kim Poktae during the campaign against
the Sambyŏlch'o Elite Corps. Kim had disciplined each of the them
at least once for breaking military regulations. If that had indeed
been the cause of deep resentment, Kim Pang-gyŏng should have

had countless enemies. He had been a strict commander; he had to be strict in order to prevent troops of a weakened nation from degenerating into brigands.

Soon it was the year 1278, the fourth of King Ch'ungnyŏl's reign. After delivering his New Year's congratulations to the king, Kim Pang-gyŏng stated his wish to resign his post.

"The two recent cases of slander point to the fact that those who administer the nation are not of one mind," Kim said. "I believe that Wi Tŭgyu and his cohorts castigated me to give vent to personal rancor. Who could have imagined that the chief minister of state could be tried in the manner that I was? It happened because Yuan officials have the power to dictate our nation's affairs at their whim. If the men of our own government are of two minds, we are likely to have other incidents that may destroy the integrity of our government. My absence from the ranks of ministers will benefit our nation more than my continuing presence."

The king did not allow Pang-gyŏng to resign. Although Pang-gyŏng had spoken of "two minds," the king knew that a collective third "mind" intruded into Koryŏ's internal politics. The combined prerogative of Khutlgaimish's *kelinkou,* Chang Shun-lung, Yin-hou, and Che-hsin, had grown such that the three monopolized the function of emissary to the Yuan court. The influence they wielded as Koryŏ's link with the Yuan Imperial Secretariat had to be reckoned with. Supported by Queen Khutlgaimish within and bolstered from without by the Yuan secretariat, they flaunted their presumed power with an arrogance that made them malodorous to the Koreans. Only Kim Pang-gyŏng commanded sufficient popular respect to be able to exercise some restraint over the three.

On January 16, Hong Tagu rode into Kaegyŏng at the head of one hundred cavalrymen. He had returned to Koryŏ after an absence of three years. Proceeding immediately to the royal palace, he informed King Ch'ungnyŏl that he had come to investigate points of doubt raised during the recent interrogation of Kim Pang-gyŏng and his son. Although the king insisted that all doubts had been cleared, Hong Tagu replied that the report he had received in Tung-ching indicated that the culpability of the accused had been glossed over—for which reason he had obtained Kubilai's permission to adjudicate the matter; having been appointed supreme commander for the pacification of Koryŏ in January of the previous year, he was obliged to preside at a formal trial. The tone of his appropriately courteous speech was imperious, suggesting his resolve to let no one, whatever his status, contradict him.

"The place shall be the Pongŭn Monastery, at noon, two days hence," he said to an attendant courtier.

Kim Pang-gyŏng and his son Hŭn came to the Pongŭn Monastery at the designated hour. As they entered the gate to the monastic grounds they were seized and bound like common criminals. Several Korean courtiers were present as witnesses but were impressed into silence by Hong Tagu's intimidating posture. Although Hindu was also present to sit as a judge along with Hong Tagu, he remained silent throughout the proceedings.

Hong Tagu had been Hindu's subordinate during the campaign against Japan. But now they shared the title of Supreme Commander for the Subjugation of the East and would have coequal authority in directing a second overseas expedition. As colonial administrator, Hindu was invested with supreme authority over all Mongol military colonies in Koryŏ, but Hong Tagu's authority superseded his in matters pertaining to the government of Koryŏ.

What took place on that winter day at the Pongŭn Monastery stunned the Koreans. Ordered by Hong Tagu, the guards shackled Pang-gyŏng and Hŭn at the neck and caned their heads. Tagu meant to hear his prisoners admit their intent to rebel. Exposed to the elements for long hours, the naked flesh of the prisoners gradually darkened as if suffused with ink.

The interrogation was resumed a fortnight later, on February 3, on the grounds of the Hŭngguk Monastery, a short distance from the Pongŭn. King Ch'ungnyŏl's presence was requested by Hong Tagu, who announced that this interrogation would be held in accordance with royal procedures. The king was powerless to halt what he was suffered to witness, for rebellion by a tributary state was a matter over which Hong Tagu, not he, exercised authority. The steady sleet wetted both Kim Pang-gyŏng and his interrogator. Hong Tagu's determination to force a confession was evident, but Kim was steadfast in his refusal to speak. His flesh torn and spewing blood, Kim went limp several times only to be forcibly revived.

"It is midwinter, and the sleet continues," Hong Tagu paused to say to the king. "And you must be tired. If Kim Pang-gyŏng admits his guilt, only he will be punished, and his only punishment will be exile. I cannot understand why he refuses to save his own life by having this interrogation ended."

Unwilling to see Pang-gyŏng suffer any longer, the king went to his side and pleaded with him to admit to the libelous charges.

"Why does Your Highness urge me to confess falsely?" Kim Pang-gyŏng protested, looking into the king's tear-filled eyes. "I rose from the ranks to be honored with the post of chief minister. Though my brain be dashed out and my innards spill out onto the ground, my suffering would be trivial compared to my debt of gratitude to my country. Would I dare betray the gods of our land and admit to false charges merely to prolong my life?"

King Ch'ungnyŏl did not know what the frenzied Hong Tagu so desperately sought. Kim Pang-gyŏng knew precisely. His eyes closed, he saw two faces—the pale, unspeakably cruel face of Hong Tagu and, beside it, Kubilai's, always benign and magnanimous. The two faces would alternately merge one into the other, becoming superimposed, then separate. When Kim heard Hong Tagu speaking, he also heard Kubilai speaking. Tagu's impersonal voice would acquire the qualities of the voice of the Kubilai who had awarded him the heraldic gold escutcheon. But when he visualized Kubilai's benign face, the voice he heard would become Hong Tagu's. The ruse was transparent. What Hong Tagu sought was what Kubilai sought. Yet, Kubilai might not have ordered his trial and conviction. Hong Tagu might have concocted the entire affair without Kubilai's knowledge. But Kubilai had appointed Hong Tagu to the supreme post in Koryŏ, and the working of Tagu's will was the working of the imperial will.

As the beatings were repeated with increasing severity, Kim Pang-gyŏng found himself occasionally rebounding to experience moments of exceptional lucidity. During those moments, he could read the thoughts hidden behind Hong Tagu's bloodshot eyes. Tagu was not prosecuting him for reasons of personal enmity. By extracting a false confession, by making Koryŏ's chief minister confess his intention to rebel, he would gain the pretext needed to bring the Yuan military in full force into Koryŏ. If that were to happen, *darughachi* would be stationed in all cities and Yuan troops would occupy every strategic geographical point. The Yuan Empire would annex the rest of Koryŏ as easily as it had the vast area north of Chabi Pass.

Kim gave only one answer: "Our small nation has subordinated itself to your great nation much as it would to Heaven, and we regard that great nation with the same affection that a child feels for its parents. Would we be so foolish as to defy Heaven, to turn against our own parents, knowing that such an action promises self-destruction? Though I may suffer a senseless death, I will not admit to slanderous charges. Kill me if that is what you wish." Hong Tagu, the inflicter, had began to show great fatigue. The interrogation had run its course.

The trial was brought to a conclusion shortly before nightfall. For the crime of having retained helmets in their possession, Kim Pang-gyŏng was sentenced to exile on Taech'ŏng Island, and Kim Hŭn to exile on Paengnyŏng Island. All others accused of complicity were released.

Pang-gyŏng and Hŭn appeared more dead than alive when they were carried away from the monastery grounds. Three days later when they had regained some physical strength, they were taken away from Kaegyŏng on palanquins provided by King Ch'ungnyŏl. The boulevard leading to the South Gate of the capital was crowded with well-wishers, who wept at the sight of the two palanquins surrounded by Mongol and Korean guards.

King Ch'ungnyŏl would have to inform the Yuan court of Kim Pang-gyŏng's exile. Although he wished to send his minister Yu Kyŏng, he yielded to Queen Khutlgaimish's wish to send one of her *kelinkou*. In truth, the king would have gone himself in order to perform the act of homage that had been postponed because of the disturbance within the Yuan Empire, and also for the opportunity to provide Kubilai with his own description of the cases of slander that had disturbed Koryŏ. But he could not, for Khutlgaimish was again carrying a child. Had he had dared suggest going without her, Khutlgaimish would have responded with unbridled rage. On February 10, he despatched the *kelinkou* Yin-hou.

Ch'ungnyŏl had welcomed Khutlgaimish to Koryŏ to be his queen; the late Yi Chang-yong had first suggested it, and he had come to wish it himself. He now wondered if he had been wise. He could not have known that her many Mongol attendants would arrogate key positions in Koryŏ's government. Nor could he have known that Khutlgaimish, forced to marry him in her youth, would change once she became aware of the smallness and impotence of the kingdom to which she had been sent. Her sharp temperament, which would have been remarkable in a Korean woman, might have been an inborn trait that began to surface in perverse ways when she came to know the land over which she had been consigned to reign as queen.

Whenever Khutlgaimish suffered displeasure, she threatened to return to Kubilai. She raised her whip against those who attended her, at times even against King Ch'ungnyŏl. When her heart was in turmoil she was wholly ungovernable. No one could predict when she would be stricken with rage and, if she was, when the storms of temper would subside.

Worse, Khutlgaimish was under the influence of those *kelinkou*. She issued orders almost daily, and they often contradicted those issued by the king, sometimes even those she herself had issued earlier.

Yet, the king could only conclude that his marrying Khutlgaimish had benefited Koryŏ. Surely there would be another war with Japan. Koryŏ thus far had been assessed the task of making arrows, but exempted from providing ships and other implements of war. It all seemed too good to be true, especially when he recalled what had preceded the earlier invasion: first, a Mongol emissary had come to inspect Hŭksan Island in 1268; Kubilai had thereafter insisted that Koryŏ comply with his rules governing protectorates, demanding that a population registry be drawn up in anticipation of war with Japan, then levying the wealth of the land; in February of 1271 he had issued an edict establishing Mongol military colonies in Koryŏ, after which Koryŏ had been taxed beyond the limits of her resources. But then Kubilai seemed to have changed. He had not called on Koryŏ for military assistance even though the Yuan Empire was hard pressed to quell an insurrection—surely because Koryŏ's queen was his own daughter.

King Ch'ungnyŏl expected to gain much from his travel to the

Yuan court together with Queen Khutlgaimish. It would be an occasion to solidify Koryŏ's status as a nation having blood ties with the Yuan Empire. He could describe the difficulties imposed on Koryŏ by the presence of colonial troops and the *darughachi*. He would have an opportunity to state all his wishes and, perhaps, have them granted.

In February Queen Khutlgaimish gave birth to a princess, and the courtiers all assembled at the palace to offer their congratulations. The king took advantage of the happy event to declare an amnesty, returning the aged Kim Pang-gyŏng from exile, although not his son, Hŭn. He also ordered all government officials, from the chief minister on down, to begin wearing Yuan court apparel and to adopt the Mongol style of coiffure.

The matter of coiffure and dress had been an issue once before. When Khutlgaimish had come to Kaegyŏng, the king had ordered her Korean escorts to style their hair as the Mongols did. He had further urged his courtiers to adopt Mongol customs, but those who did soon abandoned them. Only the king and his close attendants wore Tartar clothes and affected the Mongol style of head-dress. A Korean male could not bear having the forward half of his crown completely shaven save one small isolated lock of hair. Even the donning of Tartar clothing required some determination. Pang-gyŏng had urged the king to issue such an order if it would benefit the kingdom. The ministers and courtiers complied promptly, encouraging the rest of officialdom to follow suit. But the youths of the Royal Academy refused. The eminent senior scholar Pak Hang summoned the superintendent of the academy and spent several days patiently dispensing admonition. Only then did the students agree to comply.

On March 11, Yin-hou returned from the Yuan Empire. Every member of the royal court was present to hear his report. Kubilai wished the king and queen to present themselves at the Yuan court when the warmth of spring returned, and he would recall Hong Tagu from Koryŏ. For once the Koreans felt their hearts gladdened.

Yin-hou related Kubilai's many questions concerning Kim Pang-gyŏng. Kubilai had asked him the number of helmets Kim had been accused of hoarding. When he replied, "Forty-six," Kubilai laughed. Pang-gyŏng is a brilliant commander, Kubilai continued, and would know better than to consider rebelling with only a few dozen helmets for equipment; further, because tax rice from the provinces must be shipborne on the route of delivery to the capital, Pang-gyŏng's shipbuilding and loading of grains should not have aroused suspicion; and if Pang-gyŏng had been inclined to rebel, surely he would not have built a new residence in the capital.

According to Yin-hou, Kubilai's final remark was, "I shall call Tagu home. Let the king of Koryŏ come to pay homage when the grasses in the fields have grown tall."

Kim Pang-gyŏng, in attendance at the royal court for the first time since his return from exile, marveled at the quickness with which Kubilai evaluated evidence and made judgments. He was surprised to learn that he held Kubilai's trust, and amazed that Kubilai would recall Hong Tagu, an action that would be consistent with logic. Knowing that Kubilai had upheld him, Kim felt the Mongol emperor's protective aura about him, and he felt a certain warmth. Naturally he wondered if he had erred in judging Kubilai's character. Perhaps that presumed identity between Kubilai and Hong Tagu had never existed. And yet, when he remembered Hong Tagu's arrogance and the confidence with which he committed outrages, he remained convinced that Tagu was controlled by the will of another far greater and more powerful than Tagu himself.

King Ch'ungnyŏl, indeed everyone at court, was transported by the news of Hong Tagu's imminent departure from Koryŏ.

"The son of Heaven is benevolent and wise," the king said. "He has clarified the difference between suspicion and truth."

Kim Pang-gyŏng glanced at the figure next to him, that of the aged minister Yu Kyŏng, whose head touched the floor as his body heaved to great, silent sobs.

"His Imperial Majesty has said that he will summon Hong Tagu back to Yuan," Kim said. "Should it be true, our nation may rejoice. Now we must pray that it will happen soon. A delay of even one day may make a difference. With Hong Tagu in our land, calamity may strike us at any time." Kim had not become ecstatic as the others had. Whether the son of Heaven was benevolent and wise would be determined by whether or not Hong Tagu was actually removed from Koryŏ.

Kim's skepticism was borne out almost too quickly. King Ch'ungnyŏl had decreed that a ceremonial discussion of Zen be held in April. Hong Tagu informed Shih-mo T'ien-ch'ü that the Buddhist ritual was meant to place a curse on the Yuan Empire, and he sent the imperial secretariat a report to that effect. Kim was made privy to this information through the goodwill of the *darughachi* Chang Kuo-kang. Chang advised prudence—that the Buddhist ritual not be conducted.

The king and Kim Pang-gyŏng promptly circulated an announcement canceling the event. The king despatched No Yong as his emissary to answer to the charge lodged by Hong Tagu. Not long after, the king learned of the complicity of Wi Tŭgyu and No Chinŭi, both slanderers of Kim Pang-gyŏng. Those two men had been seen frequently in Hong Tagu's company. But Hong's presence in Kaegyŏng prevented the king from questioning those men, much less apprehending them. Wi Tŭgyu and No Chinŭi appeared to be playing the role of traitor well, as Ch'oe T'an had, but with greater cunning.

On March 16, King Ch'ungnyŏl despatched the *kelinkou* Chang Shun-lung and two others to herald his coming to the Yuan Empire.

*

Hong Tagu and Hindu invited the king to a banquet to commemorate his forthcoming visit to the Yuan court. The king was obliged to attend the banquet held within his own palace despite his great reluctance to share Tagu's company. By virtue of his title, Supreme Commander for the Pacification of Koryŏ, Hong Tagu was the king's equal. So too were the *darughachi* and the colonial administrator. Protocol required that the king seat himself in a position of coequal honor whenever he met with them. He had petitioned the imperial secretariat, hoping that his marriage to Kubilai's daughter would be considered reason enough to be relieved of this humiliation, but had been told that a change was not warranted. He needed a formal proclamation designating him Imperial Son-in-law and King. He would try to persuade Kubilai to confer that title on him.

"If Your Highness attends the Yuan court," Hindu said, "His

Imperial Majesty will probably inquire about Chief Minister Kim. What will you tell him?"

"I shall relate only what has actually happened," King Ch'ung-nyŏl replied. The Yuan official was apprehensive, and this knowledge gave Ch'ungnyŏl satisfaction. Hong Tagu, no different than usual, offered congratulatory remarks in a manner that accorded well with protocol.

King Ch'ungnyŏl and Queen Khutlgaimish left on the first of April with an entourage of more than four hundred. Kaegyŏng was festive as all members of royalty and officialdom and their spouses escorted the procession to the edge of the city and beyond.

The king rode his steed and the queen was carried in a colorful Tartar carriage guarded fore and aft by units consisting of two hundred foot soldiers and cavalrymen. Following were a number of female attendants in carriages and many more on horseback, visibly uncomfortable in sidesaddles. The procession, grander than any the people had ever seen, moved slowly northward across the sunswept plain. It was the season when the damson plum, peach, and forsythia were in full flower.

The king thought back to when his father, the late King Wŏnjong, had left Koryŏ for the first time, bearing an instrument of surrender to the Mongols. His father, then the crown prince, had been forty-one years old. King Ch'ungnyŏl, leaving the capital at the head of a similar royal procession nineteen years later, was forty-three. When his father's party of less than fifty men left for the land of the Mongols to formalize the surrender, gloom had hung heavily over the well-wishers who followed the procession to the outskirts of the city. The month, Ch'ungnyŏl remembered, had been April, but he had no recollection of flowers in bloom. Because the nation's treasury was depleted, officials of the first four court ranks had each contributed one *kŭn* of silver, and those of the fifth and lesser ranks one roll of cloth each to defray the expenses. Not many more than three hundred horses were left in all of Koryŏ, and only the crown prince and a few important retainers were mounted. The travelers had been forced to buy additional horses from their countrymen along the road of travel. King Ch'ungnyŏl marveled at the difference a generation's time had brought. His nation was still poor, but the royal procession this day was elaborate and colorful, befitting Koryŏ's dignity as a kingdom.

The party traveled at a leisurely pace lest Khutlgaimish suffer fatigue. They passed Tongnyŏng-pu and were still on a northerly course when they encountered the *kelinkou* Chang Shun-lung, who was returning from his mission to the Yuan Empire.

Chang had met with key officials of the imperial secretariat and learned about the charges lodged by Hong Tagu and Kubilai's response to them. Although Chang and the other *kelinkou* shared the flaw in character of aspiring to undeserved wealth and authority, they were able to bring back information which Korean emissaries could not dream of obtaining. Chang had duplicates of the two brief reports Hong Tagu had submitted to the imperial secretariat. The first stated:

> Kim Pang-gyŏng has accumulated grains, built ships, and hoarded a great many helmets—surely indications of his plan to initiate deviant action. I ask that our armed units be posted at all strategic points south of the capital (Kaegyŏng), that a *darughachi* be assigned to the capital of every province, that Pang-gyŏng and his male heirs be brought to our capital and degraded to slavery and that their lands be confiscated to provide food for our troops.

The second stated:

> Although Koryŏ has accepted the status of protectorate, her people remain restive. Let two thousand seven hundred men from among our veterans of the Japan campaign be placed under the command of a senior official *(darughachi)* and be deployed in Ch'ungch'ŏng and Chŏlla provinces so that they can pacify that barbarous land (Japan) and restore tranquility among the people (Koreans). Let foot soldiers collect farm oxen and implements for the purpose of developing colonial areas next year, and let Koryŏ provide the needed food and cattle feed. I submit the above recommendation to the Bureau of Military Affairs.

Hong Tagu had obtained a reinforcement of three thousand men for the defense of Koryŏ, and two thousand five hundred of them had crossed the Yalu River. But Kubilai had abruptly recalled them. Tagu had also requested that a *toktogesun,* a station for inspecting travelers, be established in Cholla province, but Kubilai had denied that request.

The knowledge of Hong Tagu's deviousness inflamed King Ch'ungnyŏl. Koryŏ would be spared adversity only because Kubilai had disapproved Tagu's proposals. Tagu had already established a *toktogesun,* and its effect on Koryŏ had been discussed several times at the Koryŏ court. This was an instance of a summary process initiated by Tagu without Kubilai's approval.

Chang Shun-lung, in addition, carried Kubilai's summons ordering Kim Pang-gyŏng and his son Hŭn, Wi Tŭgyu, and No Chinŭi to present themselves at his court. The king was delighted, for Panggyŏng's son would perforce be released from exile. Indeed, he was elated by all that Chang had reported. Surely, he thought, Koryŏ as well as himself now rested securely within Kubilai's protective aura. Perhaps all of Koryŏ's wishes would be granted, one by one, after he had met with Kubilai.

The party crossed the Yalu River and came to Tung-ching. There they encountered a vernal deluge that forced them to suspend travel for three days. On their last night in Tung-ching, a courier from Kaegyŏng brought the king a letter from Hindu, who wished the king and queen a safe journey, and told of his forthcoming recall to the Yuan Empire. It concluded: "I have been in Your Highness's country for seven years, during which time Koryŏ has had only misfortune. Nevertheless, I send you my best wishes on the occasion of your meeting with His Imperial MaJesty." The king held no particular grudge against Hindu, who at times had prodded him into complying with harsh measures but had done so only in his line of duty. Hindu's inability to restrain Hong Tagu had been vexing to Ch'ungnyŏl, but essentially he was a man possessing neither goodness nor evil. Tidings from such a man gave the king pleasure.

The king and queen of Koryŏ arrived at the site of Kubilai's imperial train, Shang-tu (K'ai-p'ing), in mid-June. The journey had taken half a month longer than the time it ordinarily took to travel this distance.

Ch'ungnyŏl and Khutlgaimish were received by Kubilai on June 17. The king, accompanied by his vassals Wŏn Pu, Yi Punhŭi, Pak Hang, Song Pin, and Kang Yunso, entered the palace garden through the southeast gate. Khutlgaimish, holding a small scarlet parasol overhead, entered from the northeast gate together with the lady of the lord of Yŏngnyŏng and a number of highborn Korean girls and joined the king's party in the inner garden. King Ch'ungnyŏl presented the emperor with tableware fashioned from gold and silver and a quantity of finely woven ramie, then entered the palace by the eastern approach; Khutlgaimish entered by the western approach. Khutlgaimish brought her children into the presence of her mother, Queen Asujinhatun, whom she presented with ten silver pieces and twenty bolts of finely woven ramie. The queen, whose resemblance to Khutlgaimish was startling, laid her hand gently on the infant prince's head. She presented him with a wine cup and a short sword, and Khutlgaimish with a carriage painted in as many hues as the rainbow.

Khutlgaimish then took her children into the presence of the Yuan crown princess, a corpulent woman, who rested her proud but dispassionate gaze on the Korean crown prince.

"Do you like the name Ijilbuha?" she asked abruptly. Thus did the infant prince acquire his Mongol name.

On the following day, King Ch'ungnyŏl presented the imperial secretariat with a petition explaining at length the slandering of Kim Pang-gyŏng and the distortion of the purpose of the Zen Buddhist ritual which he had been obliged to cancel. His statement on Kim's behalf concluded: "We sent Pang-gyŏng into exile to save his life but later allowed him to return because of his advanced age and debilitation. To think that His Imperial Majesty, in his all-pervasive wisdom, has decreed that Pang-gyŏng present himself at his court! Humbly I state my wish that you, honored secretary, will compare my statements with those submitted by the *darughachi,* and that you will provide His Imperial Majesty with your good opinion."

In early July, Ch'ungnyŏl met again with Kubilai. Unlike the previous occasion, which was a congenial meeting of families, this was a formal audience in which the Yuan emperor would query the king

of a tributary nation regarding affairs of state. Ch'ungnyŏl intended
to press Kubilai to pass judgment on the issues he had raised in his
petition.

Instead of promptly addressing those issues, however, Ch'ungnyŏl began with remarks he thought would be appropriately diplomatic: "When I learned that you had ordered your armies northward, I quickly asked that I be allowed to assist in the campaign.
Because the battle zone was so distant, Your Majesty did not grant
me permission. Should you wish to resume your campaign along
the northern border, I should like to provide assistance."

"Those are good words, but the northern fringe of the empire
has been pacified," Kubilai answered.

Ch'ungnyŏl was somewhat unsettled by the terseness of Kubilai's
reply. He continued nevertheless: "In this large world, only that
small island nation known as Japan, relying on its insularity, dares to
be arrogant. The day will eventually come when the Japanese will be
taught to bask in your Imperial benevolence. I shall make every
effort to be of assistance, and I only await your command."

"Discuss this with your ministers upon returning home and then
inform me," said Kubilai. Ch'ungnyŏl was further unsettled by
what he judged to be the curtness in Kubilai's reply. Kubilai seemed
wholly unlike the imperial father who had worn a benign expression
throughout the audience a fortnight earlier. He made no mention of
the issues which Ch'ungnyŏl had raised in his petition. Just when it
seemed that Kubilai was terminating the audience, he turned
abruptly to the Koryŏ interpreter Kang Suhyong and asked, "What
is the custom regarding dress in Koryŏ?"

"We don Tartar apparel on formal occasions but wear Korean
clothes on others," Kang replied.

"Did you think I had banned Korean dress?" Kubilai asked. "I
have never said a word about it. Why in your country have you
restricted the wearing of your own costume?" Ch'ungnyŏl was
silenced by this question.

Ch'ungnyŏl afterward was quite unhappy. He could not understand Kubilai's displeasure. Perhaps what he had presumed to be
agreeable diplomatic remarks had annoyed Kubilai. Yet he knew that
platitudinous remarks were customarily offered at the beginning of

such interviews. He entered another request for an audience, for he had thus far accomplished none of his self-assigned tasks. He did not wish to part with Kubilai on such a disheartening note.

At the next meeting, held following a day's interval, Ch'ungnyŏl related only his wishes: "You sent the Imperial Princess to become my bride, thus favoring my modest nation with a divine kindness that has instilled new hope in my people. But we have Hong Tagu, a most undesirable presence. He controls the military, interferes in our domestic affairs, and has been arbitrary and despotic in every matter he has overseen. He has established an office of the *toktogesun* in southern Koryŏ without my knowledge.

"If the Yuan military must remain in my modest nation, I ask that either Tartar or Chinese troops be despatched. The size of the army is not my concern, but the kind and quality are. The people of Koryŏ without exception pray for the removal of Tagu's army of expatriate Koreans."

Ch'ungnyŏl was aware of the vehemence of his statement. He knew that his merely mentioning the name Hong Tagu would betray his intense hatred of the man, but he wished to be candid.

"Recalling Tagu will be a simple matter," Kubilai said, having listened thoughtfully. "And what of Hindu?" he asked.

"Hindu is a Tartar. I consider him to be good of heart. But he is in the midst of Tagu's detested army of expatriate Koreans, listening perennially to distorted reports. Naturally he would tend to regard at least one in ten distortions as truth. Tagu is the source of difficulty, not Hindu. I beg that Tagu and his army be removed from Koryŏ and replaced by an army of Tartars and Chinese."

Ch'ungnyŏl wanted this wish granted even at the cost of all his other wishes.

"If that is your wish, it shall be done," said Kubilai. After the audience, Ch'ungnyŏl thought of much more that he should have related. He incorporated them in a statement addressed to the imperial secretariat.

In my modest nation, men with distorted minds, wishing to vent their peevish resentments, have used clever words to fashion slander and written unsigned letters to accuse others of an intention to rebel.

Yuan officers and the *darughachi* have subjected the accused to interrogation and torture, a procedure which has disquieted my nation.
Should similar accusations again be made, I ask that I be allowed to
investigate the charges and present my findings to the higher offices
lest the Yuan Imperial Army be given an ostensible reason to take
actions that will startle my people.

We also have evil men plotting to plunge the nation into disorder.
They have repeatedly and falsely proclaimed their intention to move
our capital back to Kanghwa Island. I ask that an army of colonization
be stationed on Kanghwa, thereby muzzling those who have proclaimed falsely.

The Supreme Commander for the Subjugation of the East has
established an office of the *toktogesun* in Chŏlla province and has
reported the following to the higher office: "Many Koreans without
proper permits travel about freely, riding horses reserved for use only
at post stations. Some have taken to ships to transport units of armed
men. Such acts, I fear, may be a prelude to insurrection. As a preven-
tive measure I have despatched an official with a detachment of four
hundred men to be placed in the service of the *toktogesun*."

My modest nation, however, had petitioned the imperial secretariat and received authorization for the king to issue permits to those
wishing to travel within the country. Since that time, all our couriers
have carried proper credentials. Who would dare take to illicit travel?
The supreme commander has worded his petition skillfully; without
imperial sanction he has installed a *toktogesun,* to which he has
assigned a detachment of four hundred men. Also of dubious character is the *darughachi* of Cheju Island, who has improperly authorized
the appointment of officials to oversee post stations along the southern coast of Naju. Can it be said that a systematic chain of command
exists at all? In all humility I ask you, honored secretary, to convey the
above to His Imperial Majesty for his enlightening judgment.

Several days thereafter, Kim Pang-gyŏng and his son arrived in
Shang-tu accompanied by some one dozen retainers. The toll which
the recent mishaps and the rigor of travel had taken of the aged chief
minister was evident in his haggardness. Wi Tŭgyu arrived a few days
after that, also accompanied by some one dozen retainers; a few
nights later he suddenly developed a fever so intense as to shrivel his
tongue, and was dead the next morning. Na Chinŭi, too, had left

Kaegyŏng for Shang-tu but had fallen ill and died on the road of travel.

On July 7, Kubilai's judgment of Kim Pang-gyŏng's trial was conveyed to Ch'ungnyŏl through the imperial secretariat:

> Since both accusers of Kim Pang-gyŏng have died, there can be no judiciary confrontation. I was already convinced of Pang-gyŏng's innocence. I exonerate him. I shall recall from your kingdom Hindu, Hong Tagu, the colonial armies, and the army of pacification in Happ'o.

The king read the edict and handed it to Kim Pang-gyŏng, who glanced eagerly at it. Only then did King Ch'ungnyŏl feel the intensity of the emotions pervading his entire being. The coming of the Mongol princess Khutlgaimish to Koryŏ had indeed been a blessing, even though that blessing had not become a manifest reality until three and a half years after her arrival. His every wish had been granted. His marriage to Khutlgaimish was not, of course, the entire reason for Kubilai's benevolence, but surely it was the predominant one. Kim lifted the edict high, handed it back to the king, then maintained a reverent silence, his head bowed low. Kubilai had become an even greater enigma—so much so that Kim felt tempted to inspect the reverse side of the sheet, as he might look behind a mask, to detect the traits that lay concealed in the man.

Ch'ungnyŏl promptly requested an audience to express his gratitude. The next day he presented himself at the imperial palace, accompanied by Kim Pang-gyŏng.

"I had requested that Tagu's army be withdrawn. Not only did you grant my wish but you also ordered the withdrawal of all Yuan armies. Being so overwhelmed with gratitude, the only words that occur to me are those wishing you longevity lasting a myriad years."

Although Kubilai said little, a gentle smile played on his lips as he listened. Ch'ungnyŏl then mentioned what Kim had urged him to emphasize—that withdrawing armies not take Koreans back with them as captives.

"My orders touch upon that, so you need not worry," Kubilai replied. "Your people will not be molested."

With Kubilai being so agreeable, Ch'ungnyŏl felt obliged to offer ingratiating remarks. "If you should you wish to post one of your trusted Tartars as *darughachi,* I would have no objection."

"What need is there for a *darughachi?* You, the king, may best guide Koryŏ."

Ch'ungnyŏl, somewhat perplexed by Kubilai's seemingly infinite generosity, spoke again, intent on pleasing him. "May I ask that the Yuan army at Happ'o be kept there? It will be needed as a precaution against a possible invasion by the Japanese."

"The Japanese hardly matter," Kubilai said. "I doubt that they could harm the people of Koryŏ. Use your own men to protect your shores." He then inquired after Kim Pang-gyŏng's state of health, and asked Kim how many times they had met before. As Kim struggled to recollect, Kubilai waved his hand as if to dismiss the question.

"You have never been in Shang-tu in autumn, our best season," he said. "Come again in autumn." By then it was well past the designated time for the interview.

On July 21, Ch'ungnyŏl and Khutlgaimish went to the palace to take their leave of Kubilai, who presented the king of Koryŏ with two falcons and a gold seal that read "Son-in-law King of Koryŏ."

On the following day, the king and his entourage left Shang-tu for Pei-ching (Taming-fu) to the south. Kubilai sent a detachment of imperial guards as escorts. At Pei-ching, Prince Togon, Princess Mongutai, and a host of Mongol courtiers and officials from Yen-tu gathered to fete the travelers. The banquet was held outdoors, and performances by musicians and dancers lent gaiety to the festive air. At the king's behest, one of the attendant guards who had an especially splendid voice sang a song that extolled the Mongol emperor's benevolence. All the garrison guards, or *korchi,* were young men of proud families, and the courtliness of their deportment won much praise from the Yuan officials. Soon the scene of the banquet was bathed in the glow of a richly colored sunset. Kim Pang-gyŏng was at last convinced that the royal visit to the Yuan court had benefited Koryŏ in every imaginable way. He whispered to the minister Wŏn Pu, "You cannot possibly know how glad I am to have lived to see this day."

King Ch'ungnyŏl's party sojourned for two days in Pei-ching, then traveled eastward toward Koryŏ.

On August 23, Ch'ungnyŏl encountered Hong Tagu at a point of travel five days' distance from Tung-ching. Tagu was coming from Tung-ching en route to Shang-tu. The king had his retainers prepare a suitable meeting site on the open field.

Hong Tagu's words of greeting were appropriately cordial: he was most delighted to see the king and queen in excellent health despite the arduous journey. He had left Kaegyŏng, he said, immediately upon receiving Emperor Kubilai's order to return to Yuan to testify against Chief Minister Kim, but the need for his return had been nullified because of Wi Tŭgyu's death. He had remained idle in Tung-ching until he received orders to report to Shang-tu. This unexpected encounter with His Royal Highness was indeed an occasion for great rejoicing.

"Do you know that you and your army will soon be leaving Koryŏ?" Ch'ungnyŏl asked.

"I have not yet seen such orders," Tagu replied. "But I expect to be so ordered when I meet with His Imperial Majesty."

"Surely you're disappointed, having to leave Koryŏ with your aims only partly accomplished."

Hong Tagu responded to the sarcasm with hearty laughter. Neither King Ch'ungnyŏl nor Kim Pang-gyŏng had ever heard Hong Tagu laugh before, and they were struck by the hollowness of his high-pitched laughter.

"Koryŏ and I seem to be strangely fated," said this Korean. "I shall probably continue to visit your country in my line of duty. I doubt that my ties with Your Royal Highness and with the chief minister have been severed."

The meeting was brief. Hong Tagu bowed respectfully to the king and queen and departed. Kim Pang-gyŏng had not spoken, but neither had Tagu addressed Kim nor so much as glanced in his direction. This meeting was a humiliating one for Hong Tagu, but he seemed to have welcomed it as a test of his pride. And even those who detested him knew that he had endured it well—so well, in fact, as to discomfort them.

Leisurely travel brought the party to Tung-ching on August 28.

Two days before the anticipated crossing of the Yalu River, they encountered the *darughachi* Chang Kuo-kang, whom the king honored with a farewell banquet held on the grounds of a Buddhist monastery. The king had grown fond of this kind, honest man. Chang's fairmindedness, unusual in a *darughachi,* had earned him the trust of the Koreans. In neither case of slander had he sullied himself. Both the king and Kim Pang-gyŏng regretted his departure.

"The supreme commander and I have been ordered home," Chang said. "All units of the imperial army will be withdrawn. I consider this a blessing for your country."

The travelers crossed the Yalu River on September 7 and, for the first time in five months, stepped foot on what formerly was their native soil. On the following day, they encountered Shih-mo T'ien-ch'ü, who requested an audience with King Ch'ungnyŏl and, with surprising humility, begged forgiveness for his transgressions.

It took the party several days to cross the territories of the northern border and western seas, now a part of the Yuan Empire. From time to time the travelers saw groups of soldiers, either Mongols or expatriate Koreans. Ch'ungnyŏl speculated on the possibility of having this vast area returned to Koryŏ. Surely, he thought, Kubilai would agree to the reversion for Khutlgaimish's sake, if not his.

When they had crossed Chabi Pass, Khutlgaimish insisted on being welcomed back to the capital by the royal honor guards wearing caps emblazoned with golden floral patterns and by all ministers and officials, both civil and military, in ceremonial dress. She wished her adoptive country to honor her as her father's empire had.

The king sent Yi Sŭp to convey her wish to the court. But the minister In Kongsu, sitting at the helm of government during the king's absence, replied that the ministers and officials would be attired in their usual courtly robes lest the people be disgruntled by a needless show of ostentation. The king reasoned with Khutlgaimish and persuaded her to accept the requirements of propriety. The welcome which the royal couple received on their return to Kaegyŏng on September 24 was, nevertheless, ostentatious beyond anything the people had ever witnessed. The commanders of the three royal guard units, the commanding generals, and the royal musicians were attired in ceremonial finery. Lining both sides of the avenue from the city boundary to the Sonui Gate were all the members of the royal house and officialdom. Students of the Royal Academy and the East-West College presented the royal court with a song they had composed, praising the king and queen for having accomplished what they had believed to be impossible, the withdrawal from Koryŏ of all foreign troops.

CHAPTER 3

FOR THE first time since his accession to the throne, Ch'ungnyŏl knew the pleasure of ruling his nation without Mongol constraint. The offices of the *darughachi* and the colonial administration had been abolished. The colonial armies at Hwangju, Pongju, Yŏmju, and Paekchu, the detachment that had lingered in Happ'o since the invasion, and the armies commanded by Hindu and Hong Tagu were gone. The Koreans had fed Mongol troops for seven years. With the Mongols gone, they saw a quick accumulation of food for themselves.

Not long after his return from the Yuan court, King Ch'ungnyŏl decided to eliminate those men who had colluded with Yuan officials to bring grief to their own country. Planning his move carefully with Kim Pang-gyŏng, he ordered the brothers Yi Punhŭi and Yi Sup seized on October 4. The brothers, it was now known, were the culprits who had tried to disgrace Kim Pang-gyŏng; with Hong Tagu's backing they had manipulated Wi Tŭgyu and No Chinŭi into charging Pang-gyŏng falsely. The king condemned Yi Punhŭi to exile on Paengnyong Island, and Yi Sup on Chohol Island, and then despatched agents who drowned them in the sea.

Next, the king exiled sixteen officials who had been posted in Ch'ŏngju, including the commissioner for draft animals Son Sejŏng and the scribe Chi Tŭngnyong, the two men most detested by the people of Ch'ŏngju.

In the following intercalary month of November, the king sent an emissary to inform Kubilai of his actions. On December 5, the Mongol judge Sulka came to investigate the recent exiles and executions and an allegation that the Koryŏ government had denied

Korean spouses of Mongol troops the right to leave Koryŏ. In Sul-ka's party was one Kim Posŏng, who was known to some members of Koryŏ's court. Posŏng was a trusted retainer of Hong Tagu and had been friendly with the Yi brothers; the Koreans knew they had to be cautious. Surely Hong Tagu had had a hand in Judge Sulka's being despatched from Yuan together with Kim Posŏng.

King Ch'ungnyŏl conferred with his ministers and decided that he would go to the Yuan court and himself explain the circumstances to Kubilai.

Less than two months following his return, Ch'ungnyŏl found himself again on the road of travel. He left Kaegyŏng on December 13. Unlike his previous journey with Khutlgaimish, the royal entourage consisted of only one hundred men. Driven by urgency, the party braved the sleet and snow to arrive in Yen-tu on the twenty-ninth. Ch'ungnyŏl was not granted an audience immediately. He attended the ceremony at the imperial palace to welcome the new year, 1279, then spent many days in enforced idleness. The permission he sought was received on January 18.

After offering words of greeting to Kubilai, Ch'ungnyŏl was directed to a chair to the right front of the throne. Aligned in a row of chairs facing him were Hong Tagu, Sulka, and Kim Posŏng. The chief censor Yulelun and the vice minister of military affairs Bola entered the room and stated that they would question the king of Koryŏ as the emperor had commanded, and expected him to answer their questions candidly. The king bowed to signal his acquiescence. Bola spoke.

"Hindu and Hong Tagu have lodged a complaint that the wives and children of withdrawing Yuan army personnel were detained by your officials. Also, Kim Pang-gyŏng, an official of high rank and great authority, has flouted accepted laws. When Yi Punhŭi and his brother attempted to have him evicted from his post, Kim prodded Your Highness into having them slain. Are these truths?"

The question concerned two separate matters. Regarding the first, Ch'ungnyŏl said: "Last summer I returned to my country, bearing imperial injunctions. The supreme commander for the subjugation of the East and I, in mutual consultation, coordinated the withdrawal of imperial troops." Regarding the latter, he said:

"When the royal court of Koryŏ was located on Kanghwa Island, Yi Punhŭi at first served the tyrant Kim Chun loyally, then betrayed him. He had a hand in Kim Chun's assassination. The assassin, Im Yŏn, forced my royal father to vacate the throne. Yi Punhŭi is the culprit who instigated the affair that endangered my nation's integrity. Following my accession to the throne, the Yi brothers defied my every command. I punished them to set an example for my subjects."

Hong Tagu rose and stated his opinion: although the Yi brothers may have been guilty of transgressions, they had served their country well on many occasions; the punishment of death was inordinately severe.

"We have laws in Koryŏ that have been observed since antiquity," Ch'ungnyŏl said. "In such matters we need not heed the supreme commander."

Kubilai listened quietly to the exchange between Ch'ungnyŏl and Tagu, but presently he interrupted the two. "I am satisfied," he said, and rose from his throne.

The confrontation in the imperial presence was resumed following a day's interval. Hong Tagu demanded that Koryŏ deliver to Yuan one hundred twenty-eight wives and children of soldiers who had been recalled from Koryŏ. Ch'ungnyŏl rejected that demand, stating that girls from good Korean families had been coerced into cohabiting with Yuan troops, and that most of those wives and concubines did not wish to rejoin their men.

Having listened patiently to the heated dialogue, Kubilai said, "Korean wives who have borne children shall rejoin their husbands. Those who are childless shall remain in Koryŏ." The emperor had spoken, and both Ch'ungnyŏl and Hong Tagu bowed, acknowledging the imperial command.

"Koryŏ has its own traditional laws, and you may abide by them," Kubilai said. "However, if you must punish an official of important rank, notify me first and then mete out the punishment."

Two days later, King Ch'ungnyŏl was homeward bound from Yen-tu. Hong Tagu had been frustrated in his attempt to bring injury again to Koryŏ, and Ch'ungnyŏl dwelt secure in the warmth

he felt emanating from Kubilai. But he could not understand Kubilai's generosity to Hong Tagu, who should have been condemned
for instigating the unjust persecution of Kim Pang-gyŏng and dis-
torting information. Kubilai had seemed wholly unconcerned.
Although anyone guilty of such indiscretions deserved to be castigated, Kubilai had not spoken one reproving word to Hong Tagu.
Why had a second confrontation been held in the imperial presence
even though all differences had already been resolved? Apparently
Tagu's wish to attempt a retaliating thrust had been allowed to prevail.

The king returned home on February 10. Kim Pang-gyŏng and
the other ministers rejoiced, for what they had feared had not come
to pass. During his absence, Ch'ungnyŏl learned, Khutlgaimish had
the court musicians perform every night for her amusement. A
thousand lanterns, suspended in tiers, lit the palace grounds, and
the sounds of musical instruments filled the air until daybreak.
Once, she had a tiger released in the garden and watched its capering
from the upper floor of the pavilion. Although the king's Mongol
"guest" had borne two children, motherhood had not tempered
her fitfulness. But at least, Ch'ungnyŏl was satisfied to know, she
was gradually becoming accustomed to life within Koryŏ's royal
palace.

Khutlgaimish's *kelinkou* continued to ply regularly between Koryŏ and Yuan. The Koryŏ courtiers had once considered them
informants who took every opportunity to provide the Yuan government with a transparent view of all that was happening in Koryŏ.
They now regarded those Mongol attendants in a different light.
The *kelinkou* were providers of information about the Yuan Empire,
and they knew much about the inner workings of the imperial secretariat. Just as Khutlgaimish was gradually changing from a Mongol
"guest" into the queen of Koryŏ, so too were the *kelinkou* being
transformed from Yuan informants into agents working on Koryŏ's
behalf.

One of them, on a mission to Yuan, returned in early March
bringing important news. The last of the Sung remnants, holding
out on Ts'ui-shan Island, had been pacified on February 6. The
Sung Empire was no more. And on the very next day Kubilai had

issued orders to Chinese shipbuilders in Yang-chou, Hu-nan, Kan-chou, and Ch'üan-chou for the construction of nine hundred vessels. Kubilai was again contemplating the conquest of Japan.

A conference of ministers was called immediately. Although the ministers who had hastened to the court breathed great sighs of relief upon learning that Koryŏ had not been similarly ordered, they felt as if they were placed uncomfortably near a source of a contagion. That a second attempt would be made to conquer Japan was indisputable. Yet to be known was how Koryŏ would be affected. The majority tended to be optimistic, for the relationship between Koryŏ and Yuan had become truly amicable. If Kubilai intended to have ships built in Koryŏ, they reasoned, he would have issued such an order simultaneously with those sent to the four Yuan districts. Issuing orders piecemeal was out of character for him. He had specified nine hundred, the precise number of vessels Koryŏ had built for the first invasion, a number he probably considered adequate for a second invasion.

The ministers discussed the possibility of Koreans being conscripted as soldiers and laborers, and concluded that Koryŏ would be spared as it had been at the time of the rebellion in northern Yuan. Should they be called on to provide troops, Kubilai, being well informed about their country, would keep his demands within reason. If Kubilai thought to launch the invasion from the Korean peninsula, surely he would not have withdrawn his armies from Koryŏ.

Such optimism was due, of course, to the very special bond between Koryŏ and Yuan. Never before had the coming of Princess Khutlgaimish from Yuan been considered such a remarkable blessing as now.

Everyone was to some degree optimistic. There was no reason not to be. But a few, Kim Pang-gyŏng among them, were apprehensive. Kubilai had showered Koryŏ with too many kindnesses, Pang-gyŏng thought, quite as if he meant to impress Koryŏ with his charitable intent. It seemed unnatural. Moreover, King Ch'ungnyŏl had met with Kubilai but seventeen days prior to his issuing of the orders to construct warships. Kubilai might not have considered it to be of importance to Koryŏ, but surely an invasion of Japan merited at least a casual mention.

Another of the *kelinkou* returned from Yuan in early April. He reported that Kubilai had moved his court from Yen-tu to Shang-tu, and that the Sung general Fan Wen-hu was rumored to have received orders to "subjugate Japan." That rumor became believable when Fan Wen-hu sent two envoys, Chou Fu and Luan Chung, to Japan in the company of a Japanese Buddhist monk.

On April 25, King Ch'ungnyŏl sent the *kelinkou* Lu-ying to Yuan to fetch a physician to attend Khutlgaimish, who had been in poor health since the beginning of the year. The king had been troubled by Kubilai's complete neglect of Koryŏ, and Lu-ying had also been given the task of learning more about the planned conquest of Japan. Lu-ying sent back a courier with a message stating that he had arrived in Shang-tu on May 25. He sent no further word. On June 25 he returned to Kaegyŏng with two Chinese physicians.

Lu-ying came directly to the palace, offered the customary greetings, and said, "In accordance with a directive received from the imperial secretariat, the office of the Commanding General for the Subjugation of the East has issued these orders to Your Royal Highness." That commanding general was, of course, Hong Tagu. Ch'ungnyŏl felt a shudder pass through his body.

Tagu's orders were crisply stated: "In accordance with the Imperial wish, I order the construction of nine hundred ships for the conquest of Japan. Koryŏ shall produce the timber and proceed with the building. The King of Koryŏ shall deliberate the means of facilitation, and present his reply." Ch'ungnyŏl stared at the decree in disbelief. He read it again and again, but the figure nine hundred remained.

The king convened his ministers and read the orders. The ministers, realizing that they had been lulled into wishful thinking, stood in stunned silence. Kim pang-gyong felt hatred erupting. The object of his hatred was Kubilai, not Hong Tagu. Hong Tagu had had him shackled about the neck and caned into senselessness. Yet his hatred for Hong Tagu then was not as searing as that which flared in him now.

Kim felt his rage subsiding with a quickness that surprised him. Becalmed, he wondered why he had failed to anticipate what naturally should have followed. Kubilai had acceded too easily to their king's every wish, and, in consequence, their king must now submit to his every demand. Kim visualized that face of Kubilai which he had grown to know well, and heard Kubilai's true voice. It was a face and voice he had seen and heard dozens, perhaps hundreds, of times during the course of the first invasion of Japan. The face wore an expression no one else had ever seen, and the voice had a quality known only to him. It was the face that had floated out from the surface of written decrees and the voice that had emerged from the spaces among the words. Kim was aware that he had been remiss, having allowed them to fade from his memory.

Kim Pang-gyŏng's voice trembled as he addressed the king. "The imperial secretariat, through Tagu, has stated, 'The King of Koryŏ shall deliberate the means of facilitation, and present his reply,' " Pang-gyŏng began. "Koryŏ must send an emissary immediately to Yuan to describe the actual conditions here. Building nine hundred ships will be no easy matter. We built nine hundred vessels before, and all our mountains and plains were stripped of trees. Although we have seeded the land, how large can trees grow in five years? We shall have to seek timber in mountains so remote that they have long been considered inaccessible. Orders to build ships will inevitably lead to a levy of soldiers, seamen, and laborers. Unless we succeed in minimizing the number of men taken, males, even old men and boys, will vanish from our land. And we shall have to supply the armies that will march down the peninsula. Nine hundred ships will be built on the coast of China, another nine hundred in our country. Judging from the great size of the navy, we may expect to see armies much larger than those before coming to occupy our land."

Kim Pang-gyŏng's voice often seemed to falter but would regain its vigor when the listeners thought it would fail. The other ministers had never before heard Kim Pang-gyŏng speak at such length, and they beheld him with wonder.

"What the late King Wŏnjong and Chief Minister Yi Chang-yong had accomplished before, Your Royal Highness and we subjects must now accomplish," Pang-gyŏng continued. "Koryŏ succeeded once before, and I believe we can do so once again. We must, here and at this moment, declare ourselves unified in our intent to override this peril. Fortunately, men of treachery have been eliminated, and no countryman would repeat the follies of Im Yŏn and Ch'oe T'an. Your Highness is now forty-four, twelve years younger than the age at which your royal father passed on. Although I, senior among the ministers, am now sixty-eight, I intend to surpass the great age attained by the late Chief Minister Yi. Yu Kyŏng is my age, but the other ministers are relatively young and vigorous. Together we should be able to protect our people from the flogging to be expected from the Yuan officials.''

Among the ministers in the royal presence only Kim Pang-gyŏng spoke that day.

When deliberations were resumed the following morning, Pang-gyŏng stayed in the background, deferring to the others. The ministers selected the senior scholar Cho Ingyu and the *kelinkou* Yin-hou to serve as emissaries to the Yuan Empire. Then they talked about Tu Shih-ch'ung, who had left four years earlier as the Yuan envoy entrusted with the mission of admonishing the Japanese. Tu's party had found fair winds and set sail from Happ'o in April of 1276, but had not been heard from since then. Perhaps their ship had foundered, or perhaps they had reached Japan safely only to be held in captivity. The Koryŏ court interpreter Sŏ Ch'an was a member of that party, and all the seamen were Koreans. The ministers had often talked about the envoy's fate, but after a year or two had consigned the matter to the forgotten past.

Interest in the Yuan mission had been revived for good reason. If the envoy Tu Shih-ch'ung were to return and report favorably on the island nation beyond the barrier of wind and waves—that Japan, pledging fealty to Yuan, would send an emissary bearing an instrument of surrender—there would be no invasion. The order to build ships would be rescinded, and the office of the Commanding General for the Subjugation of the East would be abolished. The emergency pressing upon Koryŏ would recede, like the tide, into the offing.

Both the king and Kim Pang-gyŏng were intrigued by this possibility even though it seemed hopelessly remote, for "possibility" by definition implied a promise of reality. As they had once relied on Khutlgaimish to ward off calamity, they now placed their hopes on the safe return of Tu Shih-ch'ung and the felicitous tidings he might bring. Khutlgaimish was Kubilai's daughter; she had wedded their king and now dwelt in the royal palace. Important though she might be, she was powerless to steer misfortune away from Koryŏ. If her presence could not help Koryŏ, a missing envoy offered little promise of help. The ministers knew this. Yet they continued to speculate over Tu Shih-ch'ung's fate. They were not hopeful, but merely talking about an almost nonexistent hope gave them a vague feeling of comfort.

*

On July 4, Cho Ingyu and Yin-hou left for Yen-tu on a twofold mission: to be instructed by the imperial secretariat regarding the particulars of ship construction, and to protest Koryŏ's difficulties. Twenty days later, Yi Chonbi and General Chŏng In also left for Yen-tu to present the secretariat with this petition: "Recently we despatched Cho Ingyu and Yin-hou to describe the difficulties that confront us. Allow us now to enter a request: that the office of the commanding general not be authorized to supervise the building of ships. The commanding general Hong Tagu is a man who stands at odds with our country. He is detested by Koryŏ's farmers. If Tagu is named supervisor, our people will be alarmed and will flee, and we shall have difficulty fulfilling our task. We ask you, honored secretary, to convey good words on our behalf to His Imperial Majesty."

In early August, the court at Kaegyŏng was surprised to receive news about Tu Shih-ch'ung. Four men of the thirty that made up Tu's party were reported to have returned to Happ'o. Those men arrived in the capital three days later and described what had happened to the mission. The envoy's party had left Happ'o in April four years earlier and had landed at Murotsu, Nagato province, on April 15. During their detention at Murotsu, five Yuan officials were taken to Kamakura, and there executed on September 7. All crewmen were subsequently put to the sword, and only those four, from Yuan, escaped with their lives. Each told a story somewhat different from the others', but there was no reason not to believe their claim that the Japanese had killed everyone else.

The four Mongols, all in their early thirties, were so gaunt as to appear far older than their actual years. Despite urgings to remain comfortably seated, each rose when he was addressed and glanced about nervously as he spoke. They seemed to be afraid. Sweat traced glistening streaks down their darkly burned faces and necks.

King Ch'ungnyŏl sent his vassal Chi Sŏn along with the four Mongols to help them remember and recount the details of their experience. No sooner had Chi Sŏn left than a party of some one dozen Yuan officials arrived in Kaegyŏng to take stock of Koryŏ's supply of weapons.

Cho Ingyu and Yin-hou returned from the Yuan Empire in mid-August. All of Koryŏ's requests had been rejected, and the number of ships to be built remained at nine hundred. The government of Koryŏ, following a series of ministerial conferences held over the three weeks that followed, decided to begin immediately with the dread task of constructing the war vessels. The king sent provincial directors to Kyŏngsang and Chŏlla to oversee the construction, and inspectors to take charge of conscripting carpenters and laborers in Ch'ungch'ŏng, Kyŏngsang, Chŏlla, Sŏhae, Tonggye, and Kyoju provinces. Abruptly all of Koryŏ was again brought into the eye of the great storm of war.

Into the country in turmoil came the Yuan captain of the gate guards Dana and director of the archives Kabana along with several dozen subordinates to supervise the shipbuilding. The two supervisors met with the king, then went off promptly to inspect the shipbuilding sites in Kyŏngsang and Chŏlla provinces with the lord of Kwangp'yŏng Hye as their guide. Receiving and entertaining Yuan officials demanded much of King Ch'ungnyŏl's time. No sooner had Dana and Kabana left than an emissary came to Kaegyŏng to study the system of post stations. Koryŏ would have to build roads to interconnect the dozens of locations for timber production, the several shipbuilding sites, and the centers for the recruitment of workers; and a great many post stations needed to be established along the routes of transportation. Unlike the invasion of 1274, all of Koryŏ's land and people was, day by day, being organized into a system that would efficiently serve but one purpose.

Yi Chonbi and Chŏng In returned from Yen-tu in late October, and they had much to tell. Kubilai, who had taken his court to

Shang-tu in February, had returned to Yen-tu on August 2. And rumor had it that on August 10 he had summoned the Sung general Fan Wen-hu into his presence and asked him when he thought the best time to invade Japan would be. Furthermore, Kubilai must have known about the fate of his envoy Tu Shih-ch'ung. But there was no gossip about Tu's mission, hence no one knew if this new information had influenced Kubilai.

*

The new year, 1280, was the sixth since Ch'ungnyŏl's accession to the throne. Many Yuan officials attended the New Year's celebration. The two Mongols, Dana and Kabana, who had been sent to Koryŏ in place of Hong Tagu were seated at the most exalted positions in the royal room. By virtue of his position as head of the office of the Commanding General for the Subjugation of the East, Hong Tagu should probably have assumed the task of supervising the construction of naval vessels in Koryŏ, but Ch'ungnyŏl had petitioned the imperial secretariat protesting his appointment. The Koryŏ government had repeatedly sought a reduction of its obligations, but in vain. Happily, it had been granted its wish regarding Hong Tagu.

Dana excused himself from the festivities and left Kaegyŏng that day, accompanied by a Korean official, to obtain new instructions from the imperial secretariat regarding the shipbuilding. Kabana left the following day to inspect the shipyards in Chŏlla province. All of Koryŏ officialdom, from the chief minister on down to lowly functionaries, was kept constantly diligent, as were all Mongol officials assigned to duty in Koryŏ.

Dana was back in March. In February, he said, Hindu and Hong Tagu had requested orders to move out immediately at the head of the expeditionary forces but were restrained by the council of state.

Also in February, Kubilai had awarded General Fan Wen-hu a robe cut from brocade from the Western Marches of China, many silver coins, and several rolls of silk. These linked events suggested that the launching of the invasion was not far off.

The news about Hindu and Hong Tagu was disquieting. Surely

they would come to Koryŏ, as they had in 1274, at the heads of armies. The king knew about the rumor that Fan Wen-hu had received a confidential appointment to serve as a marshal in the expedition. Every Yuan official who had come to Koryŏ since the turn of the year had heard that Fan Wen-hu would command the half of the expeditionary force which would set sail from a Chinese port south of the Yangtze River. They did not doubt the truth of the rumor, for it was on everyone's lips in Shang-tu and Yen-tu. If it was true, that meant that the other half would set sail from Koryŏ, almost certainly commanded by Hindu and Hong Tagu, who would, as they had before, be in charge of mobilizing Korean soldiers and laborers.

In May, Japanese pirates attacked two port towns, taking fishermen captive. The government sent troops to the south to protect the vulnerable coastal zone. This new threat from abroad added to the woes of an already harried Koryŏ. When the southern coast was again secure, King Ch'ungnyŏl sent for Kim Pang-gyŏng.

"What would you think of my requesting orders to take part in the invasion of Japan?" he asked.

The chief minister, greatly surprised, looked directly at the king. Ch'ungnyŏl had thought the matter over carefully, and chosen participation as the only means of evading the full tragedy that had befallen Koryŏ in 1274.

"I have followed Mongol customs ever since I was crown prince," the king said. "I shaved my forehead and braided my locks, I wore Tartar clothes and married a Tartar princess. I adopted the bureaucratic system of the Mongols and renamed all of our offices and titles. Would my people now object if I traveled to Yuan and returned with orders for Koryŏ to participate in the invasion?"

Tears formed in Pang-gyŏng's eyes as he pondered the king's remarks. "It is one means," he said slowly, bowing. "I have been insensitive, failing to notice your great anguish. I beg your forgiveness.

"Such an action may well yield unexpected benefits," Pang-gyŏng continued thoughtfully. "We have been ordered to build ships but not to conscript troops and laborers, although we may expect such orders soon. If Your Highness's request is accepted before such orders are issued, perhaps we may be spared the grief that the likes of Hong Tagu would inflict on Koryŏ."

If the king's request were approved, all of Koryŏ would be mobilized to participate fully in the invasion of Japan. Koryŏ would be so mobilized regardless—in which case it seemed best to take the initiative, to risk death voluntarily in the faint hope of generating a miracle that would keep the nation alive. Moreover, the king would know the satisfaction of implementing a plan that he himself had formulated to insure Koryŏ's survival.

King Ch'ungnyŏl despatched General Pak Ŭi to Shang-tu in early June to announce his wish to present himself at the Yuan court to receive a command to participate in the expedition to subjugate Japan. He had consulted only Kim Pang-gyŏng before making his decision. Pak Ŭi was granted an audience with Kubilai on June 28. He returned to Kaegyŏng on July 22 and reported that Kubilai had consented to receive King Ch'ungnyŏl.

Later that day, the king assembled his ministers and other courtiers and announced his intention. Although both he and Kim Pang-gyŏng had thought the courtiers would protest his decision, the king's announcement was met with simultaneous, unanimous bows of acquiescence. If anything, the faces of his subjects showed relief. Regardless of the difficulty of the course on which Koryŏ would place itself, that course had been set for them. And they were released from the agony of indecision.

CHAPTER 4

KING Ch'ungnyŏl left Kaegyŏng on August 2. Queen Khutlgaimish led a host of ladies-in-waiting to the palace gate, where she bade the king farewell. Although flowers were not in season, blossoms like bellflowers graced her coiffure and those of her ladies too. It was an unusually hot summer day. The king's entourage consisting of one hundred mounted troops lacked the ostentation appropriate to royalty, but never before in the eyes of the well-wishing courtiers, who rode along with the travelers to the edge of the city, did the king present so gallant a figure as he did on that day.

The king's party raced northward on sweating horses, like a cavalry unit hastening to battle. In Tung-ching they were told that the Chinese general Fan Wen-hu, on July 29, had received orders to "subjugate the East." At a point five days' travel from Shang-tu, they were told that Hindu and Hong Tagu had received similar orders on August 9. What the king feared had come to pass. The commands to Hindu and Hong Tagu meant that Koryŏ could escape their tyranny only if Ch'ungnyŏl himself could also be commissioned at an equal or higher level of authority. The king and his vassals rode on as long as there was daylight, changing mounts frequently. They arrived in Shang-tu at dusk on August 22.

Kubilai had moved his court in May to new imperial quarters at Chagan Nor. King Ch'ungnyŏl and his men stayed that night in Shang-tu, and early the next morning resumed their travel, following a southwesterly course onto higher elevations. Soon they came to a Tartar settlement on a vast plain wafted by winds as cool as the autumn winds in Koryŏ. Tents radiated outward from the imperial residence, forming a gigantic encampment, and Mongol army units were garrisoned at points one to two miles removed from the main concentration.

On August 26, King Ch'ungnyŏl was ushered into Kubilai's presence. The palace, much smaller than those in Shang-tu or Yen-tu, was built in the traditional Mongol style, essentially a complex of tents.

Fan Wen-hu, Hindu, and Hong Tagu were also present. Kubilai awarded each of his three marshals the title of commander, Eastern Expedition Field Headquarters. The headquarters, which would control every aspect of the war to conquer Japan, would not have a fixed location, but would be shifted about so as to be situated close to its commanders.

Ch'ungnyŏl was informed that Hong Tagu and Hindu would set sail from Happ'o leading a combined army of forty thousand Mongol, Northern Chinese, and Korean troops, and Fan Wen-hu would sail from the coast of south China with one hundred thousand southern Chinese troops; the two fleets would converge off the shores of the Japanese island of Iki, then sail on as a single armada to Japan. Hong Tagu and Hindu would come again to Koryŏ; they would direct the conscription of Korean soldiers and laborers, whose fates they would control.

Fan Wen-hu simply did not look the part of a commander of one hundred thousand men. When Kubilai asked him questions, he would hunch forward and crane his neck as he listened and then indicate agreement or dissent as only he could. He would spread his arms and raise them slightly to express agreement, and, instead of saying no, would pull his head in as a turtle might, then waggle it, fanning his upraised hands in synchronous movement with his waggling head. Hindu, assuming an attitude of extreme respect, was attentive and did not speak. Hong Tagu maintained a very erect posture and kept his gaze fixed on the emperor. His eyes had acquired an even sharper gleam, and one might believe that his unusually large ears had shaped themselves over the years the better to hear Kubilai with. When he spoke, his speech was precise and clear. Ch'ungnyŏl asked that he too be commissioned to subjugate the East, and that the emperor approve seven conditions which would inspire Koryŏ's people to rally to the imperial cause:

—That the units assigned to Cheju Island be diverted to augment Koryŏ's standing army.

—That Mongol, rather than Chinese or Korean, units serve as the vanguards of the expedition.

—That Hong Tagu be given no additional command prerogatives, and that he, Ch'ungnyŏl, share in the command of the Eastern Expedition Field Headquarters.

—That each Korean general be awarded a tally issued by the Yuan Empire, certifying his authority.

—That navigators and sea hands be conscripted from the coastal regions of China.

—That inspectors be sent to Koryŏ to help alleviate the hardship of its farmers.

—That he, Ch'ungnyŏl, be present at Happ'o port to inspect cavalry horses to be taken aboard ships.

Ch'ungnyŏl carefully described the importance of these conditions. Remembering how Koryŏ had suffered before, he knew he must persuade Kubilai to accept them. He did not think his requests were unreasonable. Koryŏ would, after all, be taking part with great reluctance in a war between two foreign countries, and it would contribute nine hundred war vessels to an unwanted cause. He was not intimidated by Kubilai's presence when he stated that Mongol troops should serve as vanguards, nor by Hong Tagu's when he stated his wish to have Tagu's authority restricted.

"Let me consider them," Kubilai said, then abruptly changed the topic of conversation. "Your son and daughter took after Khutlgaimish. Are they winsome children?"

Ch'ungnyŏl said that they were becoming more winsome by the day. Kubilai nodded in satisfaction and, quite as if that were the ultimate topic of conversation, signaled the end of the audience. No sooner had Ch'ungnyŏl returned to his quarters than a messenger from Kubilai arrived, ordering him to leave immediately for Koryŏ because of the many exigencies awaiting him there.

Three days later, on August 29, King Ch'ungnyŏl paid a farewell visit to the palace of tents and embarked on his return journey. Again his party rode on, seldom resting, and arrived back in Kaegyŏng on September 28.

The king convened the court and described his meeting with Kubilai. He would wait for Kubilai's reply. Soon it was past mid-October, and Kubilai had sent no word. It was then that Kim Pang-gyŏng asked permission to resign his post. He explained that in view of the history of his relationship with Hong Tagu, there was no possibility of their working harmoniously for a common cause, and his withdrawal from officialdom would be to Koryŏ's benefit.

"Despite your age, you are irreplaceable as chief minister," the king said. "This business of the expedition to the East is urgent. How can I let you go now? The nation needs you."

Although Kim Pang-gyŏng subsequently submitted a formal written resignation, the king would not accept it.

In November, Yuan officials came to Koryŏ with greater frequency to note the progress being made at the shipyards. Ch'ungnyŏl was at last convinced that Kubilai had rejected his appeal. Because he had not been given a command, his seven stipulations must also have been rejected. Although no date had been set for the launching of the invasion, it could fall on a day less than six months away, certainly no less than a year away. Hindu and Hong Tagu would soon come to Koryŏ.

A directive of the imperial secretariat, delivered to the Koryŏ government on November 8, conveyed Kubilai's orders: Koryŏ would provide the expeditionary force with ten thousand troops, fifteen thousand seamen, and one hundred ten thousand piculs of food-stuffs. Such orders had been anticipated, but the numbers were much larger than they had expected.

The ministers of Koryŏ kept themselves in conference at the palace through the night and the next morning. Their decision could easily have been predicted: they would obey Kubilai. Virtually every adult Korean male would be sent off to war. And the people who remained would be deprived of this year's crop, soon to be harvested, so that the army of invasion could be fed.

When they left the confinement of the conference, they noticed the rays of the sun, the color of the sky, and the sound of the wind were strangely different from the day before. Kim Pang-gyŏng, who had sought to resign not many days earlier, knew that only he could mobilize and command a national army. On the following day, the king named him commander of the standing army of Koryŏ. Pang-gyŏng accepted the appointment and pledged to the king, and to himself, that he would fulfill this great responsibility. He was deter-mined to use his authority to shield the Korean people from Hong Tagu.

King Ch'ungnyŏl composed a lengthy appeal addressed to the imperial secretariat. It would be his ultimate appeal, to be conveyed to Kubilai, whose response would decide Koryŏ's fate. He restated the requests he had made to Kubilai at Chagan Nor, and he gave the specific number of Korean troops that would be available for the invasion and the specific amounts of commodities Koryŏ would be able to provide. The figures were precise to the last available man and the last available bushel of rice. Ch'ungnyŏl pledged Koryŏ's total dedication to supporting the Yuan effort should Kubilai so order it—noting, however, that Koryŏ would be deprived of its abil-ity to fulfill its pledge if it were placed under the command of Hindu or Hong Tagu, and that he, the king, must be invested with the authority to issue the necessary commands. He emphasized the need to reassign the one thousand men stationed on Cheju Island to the standing army in order to raise the troop count above the mini-mal ten thousand. With regard to arms, he wrote:

> When *darughachi* were posted throughout my modest nation, they gathered up all the bows and arrows from my people, even from those who hunted for their livelihood. The five thousand three hun-dred men who make up Koryŏ's present standing army are survivors of the earlier invasion. Many of them returned without their armor and weapons. What we have gathered and stored in our vaults will not be sufficient. The four thousand six hundred men to be added to our standing army have no equipment for soldiering. I humble myself and beseech you, honored secretary, to convey to His Imperial Maj-esty my request for five thousand sets of armor, five thousand bows, and ten thousand bow strings. . . .

The king then listed the name of every officer who deserved to be awarded the imperial tally for proven valor in battle at Chin and Cheju islands and in Japan. Finally, he wrote about Kim Pang-gyŏng:

Since assuming the office of chief minister, my faithful vassal Kim Pang-gyŏng has striven mightily to carry out commands issued by your honored imperial court. He has served your imperial army well, performing with valor at the three sites of battle, Chin Island, Cheju Island, and Japan. He has responded well to the encouragement he was given when you awarded him the heraldic tiger-head escutcheon. Soon he will be taking part in the conquest of Japan, commanding Koryŏ's militia of ten thousand troops and corps of fifteen thousand seamen. Although he will participate in directing the invasion, he is apprehensive lest his command responsibility be so restricted as to force him into making imprudent, compromising decisions. Despite his advanced age, Pang-gyŏng is sturdy of heart and spirit. He wishes again to strive to his utmost in order to repay the debt of gratitude for the Imperial benevolence bestowed upon him. I humble myself and beseech you to convey your good words to His Imperial Majesty, recommending Pang-gyŏng's inclusion among the marshals of the army so that he may attend to his duties with confidence.

The day after the king had despatched Cho Ingyu and Yin-hou to deliver his appeal, a Yuan emissary came to Kaegyŏng with a directive of the imperial secretariat informing him that Koryŏ would receive twenty thousand rolls of silk as payment for foodstuffs to be supplied to the expeditionary force. Payment in silk was better than none at all, but what Koryŏ wanted desperately was rice, however small the quantity.

November saw Koryŏ in the throes of an upheaval incomparably greater than at the time of the first invasion, as the government conscripted men to fill the ranks of its standing army and corps of seamen.

In December, the king ordered Kim Pang-gyŏng to deliver the congratulatory New Year's message to the Yuan court. Pang-gyŏng would be on a mission to learn more about Kubilai's plan of conquest and how that plan would affect Koryŏ—and he would again protest Koryŏ's adversity. He left Kaegyŏng in early December accompanied by thirty subordinates. It had been snowing heavily since the previous day, and the details of sky and land were like brushwork over a solid white. Pang-gyŏng's party was stretched out in single file, a dark chain, as it passed through the gate of the capital.

On December 20, a messenger from Cho Ingyu and Yin-hou arrived in Kaegyŏng. The two emissaries, now on their return journey from Yuan, had sent the messenger ahead with important news. Having considered King Ch'ungnyŏl's request, the Yuan government had consented to supplying Koryŏ's troops with battle uniforms and armor. It would issue strict orders prohibiting the Yuan military from molesting the people as it marched through Koryŏ. Kim Pang-gyŏng would be appointed marshal of the army. The assistant commissioners of military affairs Pak Ku and Kim Chujŏng would both be appointed generals in the army of conquest and awarded the tiger-head escutcheon. All this had been announced on December 4. Then on December 6 had come the announcement of King Ch'ungnyŏl's appointment as left minister of the Yuan Imperial Secretariat. On December 7, Koryŏ's emissaries had been told that their king would be awarded the imperial tiger-head tally symbolizing his commission as a high officer of the army for Japan's conquest.

By virtue of his long title, Left Minister of the Yuan Imperial Secretariat and Commander of the Eastern Expedition Field Headquarters, King Ch'ungnyŏl would outrank both Hong Tagu and Hindu. And Kim Pang-gyŏng, as marshal of the Eastern Expedition, would have equal command authority with Hong Tagu and Hindu. This meant that Koryŏ would not be subjected to the arrogant dictates of Hong Tagu as it had at the time of the first invasion.

As matters stood, Koryŏ was being stripped bare; it would provide Yuan with nine hundred war vessels, a militia of ten thousand men, a corps of fifteen thousand seamen, and foodstuffs amounting to one hundred ten thousand piculs in Chinese measure. But the king and Kim Pang-gyŏng now had the prestige and authority they would need in their attempt to save Koryŏ from extinction.

Cho Ingyu and Yin-hou returned on December 24. The king, accompanied by the One Hundred officials, proceeded beyond the western gate of the capital to accept formally the Yuan imperial rescript. In it was noted every award and advancement in rank which the king had requested on behalf of his vassals.

*

On January 4, 1281, orders to commence hostilities were issued to Alahan, who had been appointed right minister of the Japan district secretariat, and to marshals Fan Wen-hu, Hindu, and Hong Tagu. On that day in Yen-tu, Kubilai received his subjects at the Ta-ming Palace and accepted their congratulatory New Year's greetings. Following this ritual, Kim Pang-gyŏng was asked to attend the banquet for officials of the highest four court ranks. Kubilai bade Pang-gyŏng be seated next to the Yuan prime minister, and addressed him warmly, smiling constantly.

"I am told that Koreans are fond of these," he would say as dishes of meat and fish were served. Pang-gyŏng had already met with Kubilai twice during this sojourn in Yen-tu. He had been received in audience to express his gratitude upon being appointed marshal of the army and, again, to describe the extremely dire straits into which Koryŏ had fallen. Throughout those meetings Kubilai had kept a warm smile on his face whereas Pang-gyŏng had not once managed a smile.

Nor did Kim Pang-gyŏng smile during the banquet. The men about him smiled and laughed often, but he did not. It was not that he chose to be solemn; try though he might, he could not bring a smile to his face. The aged chief minister of Koryŏ sensed that other face of Kubilai's which he had seen in a thousand imaginings, quietly and constantly observing him. All others present at the banquet were impressed with the polite, subdued image Pang-gyŏng projected.

On his departure from Shang-tu following three days of festivities, Kim Pang-gyŏng was given formal orders to "subjugate the East." His army of Korean troops, designated the Third Army, was to be combined with the Second Army, which Hindu and Hong Tagu would lead from the Yuan Empire through the Korean peninsula to Happ'o, the port of embarkation. The Second and Third armies, Kubilai emphasized, were to constitute a unified command. The First Army, under the joint command of Alahan and Fan Wen-hu, would set sail from the coast of China. The two fleets would rendezvous off Iki Island, then sail together to Japan. Pang-gyŏng was awarded a set of bow and arrows, a sword, and armor overlaid with white feathers, and for distribution to his troops, one thousand bows, one hundred sets of armor, and two hundred battle garments.

Kim Pang-gyŏng arrived home in early February and reported to the king. Then in the king's name he ordered the army of Koryŏ into action.

On February 10, unit commanders of the Yuan army presented themselves at the palace to take their leave of Kubilai, who spoke these words of admonition: "Long ago, that nation sent envoys to us, and so we sent our envoys to them. They refused to allow our envoys to return. You esteemed men shall teach them to behave correctly. The Chinese have a wise saying: 'One nation conquers another because it covets the latter's land and peasantry. Of what use would the land be if the peasantry is killed off?' I have another concern—your fear that they will not be amicable. Should men of that nation approach you to initiate talks, consult one another so that you can give them one reply."

The Second Army, commanded by Hindu and Hong Tagu, marched out of Yen-tu soon thereafter. On March 16, two days before the Second Army's scheduled arrival in Koryŏ's capital, Kim Pang-gyŏng led his army of two thousand Korean troops out of Kaegyŏng. At Happ'o it would rejoin the larger contingent of five thousand Korean soldiers that had left earlier. Pang-gyŏng's army would be augmented by several units, each numbering in the hundreds, billeted along the route of its march. The sky above was overcast as the first unit of Pang-gyŏng's army marched out of the parade ground by the capital's South Gate, followed at measured intervals by the second, then the third unit. Only women and the very aged lined the road of the march. Some were seeing off their kin. But most wore a blank expression—they had already bade farewell to their husbands and sons. Occasionally, piercing shouts and wails were heard from grieving women and old men, their heads pressed against the earth.

The capital the next day was like a deserted city. There were no soldiers, no neighing of horses. The streets were empty but for urchins—some with their heads shaved, leaving one isolated lock that sprouted from a spot far above the brows, others with full heads of hair and bangs trimmed evenly across. The difference

between Tartar and Korean hairstyles may have been conspicuous in
the eyes of adults, but seemed unnoticed by the children themselves, who delighted in jostling and chasing one another. In other
respects they were identical: very pale, with grimy hands and feet,
dressed in tatters.

On the following day, a Yuan emissary's party was seen riding up
the great thoroughfare of the capital. The emissary, the court of
Koryŏ knew, brought Kubilai's rescript proclaiming King Ch'ungnyŏl of Koryŏ "Son-in-law and King." Ch'ungnyŏl stood before the
western gate of his palace to welcome the emissary. When he and
Khutlgaimish had visited Shang-tu in 1278, Kubilai had given him a
gold seal inscribed with the words "Son-in-law and King of Koryŏ."
Now Ch'ungnyŏl was formally authorized to proclaim that title.
The implications were profound: Koryŏ was now a kingdom ruled
by Kubilai's acknowledged son-in-law; the empire and the kingdom
were formally bonded in a father-and-son relationship.

In the spacious setting of the palace compound, the men of Yuan
at first appeared quite small in stature in the eyes of the courtiers
who stood at the far end of the grounds. They approached the palace, moving in a column led by an officer who held aloft a large
tubular metal container for imperial rescripts. A whirlwind playing
about the grounds raised swirls of dust several times in the path of
the emissary's party, cutting it off from the view of the courtiers,
and the men of Yuan appeared gradually magnified each time they
emerged from the curtain of dust.

The next day, the quiet of Kaegyŏng was broken by the incursion
of thirty thousand soldiers of the Yuan Second Army. The streets of
Kaegyŏng were again congested with men and horses. Every dwelling was vacated to provide quarters for the men in the command of
Hindu and Hong Tagu, and their occupants found refuge in Buddhist monasteries scattered throughout the hills more than a mile
west of the city. The faraway din raised by the troops and horses
could be heard by those refugees.

Hindu and Hong Tagu proceeded to the royal palace immediately. For the first time at a meeting with those two did the king seat
himself in a position of superiority, facing south. He had been
obliged until then to treat them as his equals, but his status had

been elevated the day before. He would no longer suffer the indignity of being seated with them on an east-west axis. Hindu appeared somewhat bewildered when he came into the king's presence, but not Hong Tagu, who went straight to the appropriate chair without hesitation or loss of composure. This unprecedented display of superiority by their king gladdened the hearts of the Koryŏ courtiers who witnessed the meeting.

In a discussion that was surprisingly brief, the three men decided how the Second and Third armies would be integrated. Each had been appointed commander of the Eastern Expedition Field Headquarters and therefore held equal authority with the others in devising military strategy.

Two days later, on March 20, Hindu and Hong Tagu led their army out of Kaegyŏng, which again became a silent city inhabited by women, old men, and urchins.

On the first day of April, King Ch'ungnyŏl and his honor guards also left Kaegyŏng for Happ'o. The king and his guards were in full battle dress. They arrived in Happ'o on the fifteenth and saw the long, narrow inlet crammed with the nine hundred war vessels produced by the blood and sweat squeezed out of Koreans over the past year and a half. The slopes of the hills rising from the inlet were occupied by clusters of units, numbering in the hundreds, each made up exclusively of Mongols, Koreans, or Chinese—men of three races whose differences were discernible in their facial features and deportment.

The king established his temporary quarters on the grounds of a monastery halfway up a slope overlooking Happ'o harbor. He did not see Hindu or Hong Tagu that day or the next, each being preoccupied with planning the orderly embarkation of the men under his command.

At dawn on April 17, the troops began to board the ships, and the embarkation was completed at dusk. Once the tens of thousands of soldiers were shipborne, the land was strangely quiet. The sound of waves lapping the shores could be heard at the monastery where the king lay down for a night's rest.

On the following day, however, all men were ordered to disembark and stand in formation on the broad stretch of sand at the southern end of the harbor. King Ch'ungnyŏl rode at the head of the marshals and subordinate commanders inspecting the thirty thousand Mongol and Chinese troops and the ten thousand Korean troops of Kim Pang-gyŏng's Third Army. Aligned in countless rows alongside Koryŏ's standing army were the many contingents of Koryŏ's supporting corps of seamen, fifteen thousand in all. The Koreans were visibly inferior to the Mongols and Chinese in the quality of their dress, armor, and weaponry; and their movements were less snappy. Moreover, there was a wide range in their ages; some of the older men were clearly in their sixties while the youngest were mere adolescents.

The men were to have boarded the ships two or three days following the inspection, but inclement weather caused another few days' delay. When at last they were aboard, the departure was postponed several times. The fleet finally set sail at dawn on the third of May. One hundred fifty of the two hundred vessels carrying Korean troops were the first to leave the inlet for the open sea. The ships carrying Mongol and Chinese troops followed, and the other fifty ships of the Korean fleet were the last to clear the harbor. The surface of the inlet was now covered evenly with ripples. The wind, suddenly cold, was wintry, but the sky overhead was cloudless.

*

King Ch'ungnyŏl stayed in Happ'o. He was responsible for issuing replies to communications from the departed fleet. In June he briefly visited Kyŏngju, once the capital of the ancient kingdom of Silla. The city, lying mostly in ruins, was soundless. The king rode out to the nearby plains, which were dotted with burial mounds containing the remains of Silla's royal family, and came to the Pulguk Monastery on the skirt of a mountain. The monastery, too, lay in ruins, and its vast grounds were deserted. The two famous stone edifices—the Sakyamuni Stupa and the Stupa of Many Treasures—stood in serene silence, basking in the warm sun of early summer. The king remained in Happ'o until July, then returned temporarily to Kaegyŏng. After a month's stay, he returned to Happ'o in the intercalary month of July, riding through Kyŏngsang province.

When he stopped at Annyong-pu for a night's rest, a courier came to him from Happ'o with a report that stunned him: the great armies that had set out to conquer Japan had been defeated. There were no reliable details. According to some men who had managed to return to Happ'o, the entire armada, carrying the forty thousand men from Happ'o and one hundred thousand men from the coast of south China, had been destroyed in one night by a typhoon off the Japanese coast.

King Ch'ungnyŏl hastened to Happ'o. Three days later, on the sixteenth of intercalary July, a badly damaged ship, with Kim Pang-gyŏng on board, sailed into the bay. Many of the men with him were wounded.

On the nineteenth, the king despatched General Yi In to inform Kubilai of the defeat. Surviving ships were beginning to straggle in to Happ'o. Aboard one of the vessels were the three marshals, Fan Wen-hu, Hindu, and Hong Tagu.

In the "Biography of Kim Pang-gyŏng" in the *History of Koryŏ,* it is stated:

> Pang-gyŏng, Hindu, Tagu, Pak Ku, and Kim Chujŏng set sail together, arrived at the Great Bright Bay of the nation of Japan, and admonished the Japanese through their interpreter Kim Cho. Chujŏng's unit was the first to engage Japanese warriors in battle. All other units disembarked to support him. The commanders K'ang Yen and K'ang Shih-tzu were among the casualties. In June, Pang-gyŏng, Chujŏng, Ku, Pak Chiryang, and Regional Commander Ching fought the Japanese, killing more than three hundred of the enemy. Then the Japanese charged, and the Yuan army was repulsed. Tagu dismounted and fled on foot; he was spared only because the Japanese withdrew. The Yuan army again met with defeat in the following day's battle. An epidemic had earlier claimed more than three thousand lives. At a staff meeting of the marshals, Hindu and Tagu were of like mind in advocating withdrawal because their units had suffered a series of defeats and, more important, Fan Wen-hu's fleet had failed to arrive. "The emperor had ordered the eastern fleet from Koryŏ and the southern fleet from China to meet off the coast of Iki Island at full moon in the month of June," they said to Pang-gyŏng. "The southern fleet failed to come. We arrived here first and have fought many

battles, but our ships are rotting, and our provisions will soon be exhausted. Marshal, what are your thoughts?''

Pang-gyŏng would not answer them. They met again after ten days, and the same arguments were presented. This time Pang-gyŏng replied: "In accordance with the imperial pronouncement we came stocked with provisions for three months, and we have one month's supply remaining. If we wait for the southern fleet to arrive and then attack the Japanese in full force, we will destroy them without fail." The other marshals did not press the issue. At last Wen-hu's army of one hundred thousand southern Chinese soldiers arrived in a fleet of some nine hundred ships. It met with forceful winds in August, and the entire army of southern Chinese perished in the sea.

Kim Pang-gyŏng long remembered the horror of the Japanese bay filled with corpses that successive tides brought in. Try though he might, he could not banish it from his vision. The scantily clothed bodies, their heads angled sharply downward, drifted just below the surface. The dark waters separating the corpses undulated, occasionally sending waves high into the heavens and scattering spray over the watery field of corpses.

The report of the disastrous outcome reached Kubilai at his palace in Shang-tu on intercalary July 29. King Ch'ungnyŏl, following Kubilai's directive, sent Pan Pu as special emissary to deliver consoling messages to Hindu, Fan Wen-hu, and Hong Tagu. On August 29, the king received another directive from Kubilai, ordering Koryŏ to provide food for Yuan survivors. At the end of the month, the three Yuan marshals left Kaegyŏng for their home country.

Both Koryŏ and Yuan initiated measures to set up defenses against retaliatory raids by the Japanese. In September, Yuan augmented its defending forces on Cheju Island. On October 17, the Koryŏ government established the office of the Commandery for the Defense of Kimju, and appointed the *kelinkou* Yin-hou director, and the *kelinkou* Chang Shun-lung commander of the combat forces. In November, Yuan stationed post-invasion armies at Ch'ing-yuan, Shang-hai, and Kan-p'u.

The year 1282, the eighth of Ch'ungnyŏl's reign, soon arrived. On January 5, the Yuan government announced the dissolution of the Eastern Expedition Field Headquarters. On January 15, Koryŏ sent an emissary to Yuan, requesting that a detachment of five hundred Mongol troops be assigned to Kimju; the request was approved. In February, Yuan sent an army of one thousand Mongol and Chinese troops to defend Cheju Island. In April, a four-hundred-man Yuan detachment came to Kaegyŏng. Of the four hundred, three hundred forty were sent on to Happ'o to defend the port. The remaining sixty were assigned to the defense of Kaegyŏng. So decimated was Koryŏ's military that the government had to rely on the Yuan army for a mere sixty men to defend its national capital.

The conquest of Japan was revived from time to time as a topic for deliberation at the Yuan court, but the discussions were never sustained. Kubilai died in 1294, and the issue of the conquest of Japan was forgotten.

EPILOGUE

AFTER the abortive invasion, the tranquility of the Yuan Empire was broken by the rebellion of the Mongol princes Noyan and Kadan against Kubilai. Hong Tagu gained much glory by defeating the rebels. He subsequently rose in rank to become assistant right secretary of the regulatory secretariat for Liao-yang. He succumbed to illness in 1291, a decade after the second invasion. He was forty-eight.

Khutlgaimish died three years after Kubilai, in 1297. She and King Ch'ungnyŏl had visited the Yuan court earlier that year, and returned in May just as the peonies planted around the Sunyŏng Palace came into full flower. She had an attendant bring her a spray of peonies, and she wept as she admired them. Soon she was overtaken by illness, and was dead at the age of thirty-nine.

Kim Pang-gyŏng resigned his post following the expedition's return and lived in retirement for many years. He was eighty-nine when he died in 1300, the twenty-sixth year of King Ch'ungnyŏl's reign, but his hair was not yet streaked with grey. He was buried, as he had willed it, in the cemetery of the Andong Monastery. He had again been victimized by slander, and hence was interred without a funeral ceremony—an indignity which the king later regretted.

Koryŏ did not recover quickly from the cumulative depredation of two great wars, and King Ch'ungnyŏl's later years were largely unhappy ones. Koryŏ, too, became a victim of the disturbance created by the Mongol princes Noyan and Kadan. An army of Mongol rebels invaded the peninsula, forcing the royal court to seek refuge for a time on Kanghwa Island. The king's relationship with his son, the crown prince Wŏn, was stormy. When it was at its

199

worst, a great many of the king's favorite vassals were executed on his son's orders and the king himself was banished from the throne. After Khutlgaimish's death, the king was again able to see Queen Chŏnghwa, who had lived apart from him for fear of incurring Khutlgaimish's wrath. She eventually presented him with two daughters. King Ch'ungnyŏl died in 1308. He was seventy-three.

A NOTE ON THE AUTHOR

Yasushi Inoue was born in Hokkaido, Japan, in 1907. Since 1950, when he left the editorial desk of a major newspaper to begin a new career of professional writing, his published works have ranged from poetry, literary criticism, biography, and essays on art and history to novels and short stories on themes and subjects from legendary to contemporary times. A 1981 collection of his historical fiction alone consists of eleven volumes. Not included in that collection are at least five additional volumes of works then in progress or completed since 1981. At present he is completing a narrative of the life of Confucius; then he will begin the fourth volume of *Wadatsumi,* a historical novel of epic proportion on the theme of Japanese emigration to the United States.

Production Notes

This book was designed by Roger Eggers.
Composition and paging were done on the
Quadex Composing System and typesetting
on the Compugraphic 8400 by the design
and production staff of University of
Hawaii Press.

The text and display typeface is Galliard.

Offset presswork and binding were done by
Vail-Ballou Press, Inc. Text paper is
Glatfelter Offset Vellum, basis 50.